PREHISTORIC MAN

Prehistoric Man

A. Leroi-Gourhan

Director, Museum of Natural History, Paris

PHILOSOPHICAL LIBRARY

New York

The cover reproduces one of the most beautiful paintings of the Lascaux cave. In it an artist of the age of the reindeer shows how one of his hunting companions was felled by a bison which he had eviscerated with his long assagai.

The painting on page v shows that twenty thousand years later, in 1880, prehistoric scenes were again in vogue. The more recent artist, however, was ignorant of his ancestors! His cave, only partly covered by a leaky roof, would have been uninhabitable. And no bear would have been so rash as to attack five men at the same time. Besides, this clumsy bear seems to be using his upraised paw to give the benediction to his congregation. His opponents are no less out of character: apparently the big blond man is preparing theatrically to deal a crushing blow, not to the bear, but to his ill-fated companion! Their appearance, though elegant, is unrealistic. Men of the "age of the great bear" wore comfortable stitched clothing and not skins like these, which are more suited to Hercules or to Tarzan than to prehistoric hunters. Finally, the weapons shown in the painting are even more fantastic. In his haste to save a comrade in difficulty, the hero standing in the middle might possibly have grabbed the club which the bear is ironically brushing aside, but a good spear would have been more appropriate. And the axes wielded by the other hunters are mere toys: a piece of flint laced to a stick would have been useless in big-game hunting. Prehistoric man used better judgment and relied on his terrible ivory-pointed assagai. The only realistic part of the painting concerns the man in the background. He stands in the shadows and coldly contemplates this preposterous scene!

Seventy years of scientific progress have given us a better picture of the way of life of prehistoric man.

(Cover: plate by *Monuments historiques*.)

Translated from the original French
Les Hommes de la Préhistoire—Les Chasseurs
BY WADE BASKIN

Printed in the United States of America

FOREWORD

We know now that the human species appeared on the earth long before recorded history began. Historical times, even if pushed back to the earliest possible date, are but a few thousands of years in contrast to the millions of years that preceded. During the much longer period that preceded the earliest written or oral records—long before the familiar pattern of modern roads, cities and cultivated fields arose— our distant predecessors made their appearance.

Who were they? What do we know about them? The imagination, without the help of science, is a poor guide. The writers and artists of the nineteenth century who tried to reconstruct the primitive stages of mankind usually depicted creatures endowed with classical purity of form and living a harmonious pastoral existence among pacific landscapes. By contrast, some authors picture our prehistoric ancestor as something like a cruel, violent gorilla with almost no intelligence or culture.

Students of prehistory work with concrete facts and scientific methods. They are constantly searching for new data and formulating hypotheses. After having spent a lifetime in combing through the archives of the earth, they find it easy to understand that the Heidelberg man lived two hundred or five hundred thousand years ago while the paintings in the Lascaux cave date at most from ten or fifteen thousand years ago—in other words, from only the day before yesterday. As a result of their familiarity with the Fontechevade man, they forget that he is but a fragment of a skull. It is easy for them to visualize "Augustine" seated on the rock which she has just selected—only a glaciation and a half ago—in a cave at Arcy-sur-Cure. Augustine was a poor housekeeper; the remains of mammoths are scattered in the corners where she neglected to sweep. Augustine is known to us through only a part of her jawbone, but what a jawbone! She could probably have broken a reindeer's thigh-bone with one bite. That is enough to endow her with a strong personality.

If you ever have the urge to dig into the floor of a cave, I hope that you will remember that gate-crashers cannot gain access to Augustine's inner circle. Prehistoric personalities have their own ways of making themselves understood, but not without evasiveness. The pickaxe alone will not penetrate their secrets. There are hints, but just as in a detective story, the mystery can not be solved if the ash-tray containing the incriminating cigarette-butt has been emptied through carelessness.

If everything were so simple as these pages may suggest, there would no longer be any mystery and consequently no need for prehistory. On the other hand, one should not be deceived by the apparent complexity of the paraphernalia of a modern excavation: numerous models, hundreds of pages of notes, chemical analyses, tiny bits of bones and flint, all sorts of specimens. If there were no means of organizing and interpreting all this material, the science of prehistory could

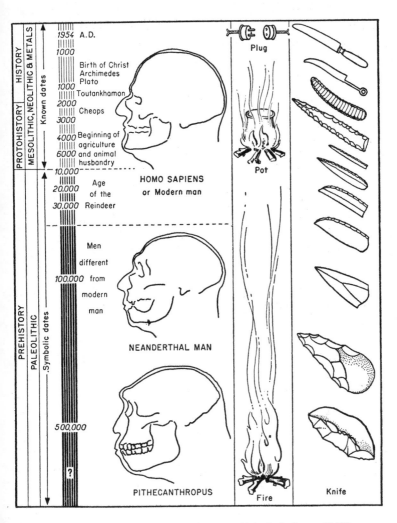

This table shows the disproportion between historical times (5,000 years, approximately) and prehistorical times (500,000 years at least). Observe the time required to pass from fire to the pot and the continuity throughout time that marks the gradual development toward perfection of a tool such as the knife.

not have been framed and would have made no progress.

This book is designed to give the reader a better understanding of the life and times of our remote ancestors. Just what did Augustine, her husband and their contemporaries do with their ten fingers during the long winter evenings deep within their cave? We can be sure that they worked hard to earn the necessary minimum of woolly rhinoceros and wild horses, and that they worked more skillfully than is commonly thought. We tend unjustly to disown the Neanderthal man with the flattened cranium and big jawbones, just as the lord of high lineage pretended not to know that the first baron's grandfather tilled the soil in the time of the Merovingians. We prefer to make a place in our genealogical tree for the artists who adorned the walls of the famous caves, forgetting that these artists owed their creativity to their low-browed cousins who during millenniums amassed and transmitted as their heritage a modest stock of knowledge.

It is not difficult to admit that twentieth-century science came from nineteenth-century science and to carry the process back to Plato or Archimedes. But before that?

Before that was the *bronze age* and, before the bronze age, the *neolithic age,* the time of the earliest husbandmen. We can still manage to picture these husbandmen as the obscure ancestors of the Greek philosophers. But before that?

Before that was the *age of the reindeer*. Then there were only reindeer hunters and salmon fishers. They had the same physical traits as we and knew how to carve bisons in stone. But they seem very remote, and we must make an effort to imagine that their mode of life had a determining influence on contemporary forms of human society. But even before that?

Before that, there were other hunters. But they did not look exactly like the men of today. The oldest of them are often described as types of superior monkeys. And this time we do not dare admit that Descartes, Lavoisier and the geniuses of the atomic age are indebted to the Pithecanthrope. But such

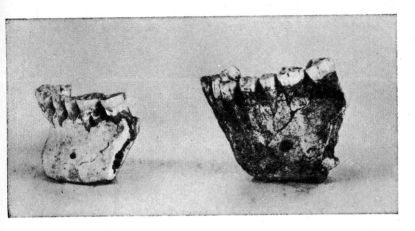

When our group discovered the first fragment of Mousterian man, one member saw fit to christen it "Augustine" in order to avoid having always to repeat: "a part of the jawbone of a very early Paleanthrope found in layer 20 of square A9 in the Hyena cave at Arcy-Sur-Cure." To repeat the complete description is rather irksome. A piece of jawbone (shown here to the left of a corresponding jawbone of a modern man) seems unimportant, but years devoted to carrying out excavations in this cavern had given us much information about its prehistoric occupants, and only a trace of the former tenant and a picturesque name were needed to give new life to our heroine.

is the fact. If the slightest gap had ever interrupted the slow acquisition of basic techniques, everything would have been to do over again. Insufficient attention is given to the continuity of the bond that ties us to an inaccessible past. We vaguely imagine prehistoric men haphazardly striking against stones to produce wretched tools and then, one lucky day, modern man entering the scene of history and everything being changed. Nothing is farther from the truth. Our classical world extends back only a few thousand years; yet to lay the foundation for it, man had worked for at least two hundred thousand years. The marvels of modern science are the fruit of long years of maturation, and these pages will show that the low-browed, thick-jawed flint-workers knew as well as we how to choose their raw material, draw up a plan of fabrication and execute the successive stages that culminate in a finished product.

CONTENTS

PREHISTORIC MAN

1. THE METHOD OF PREHISTORY

Few sciences offer such an easy approach and such an abundance of accessible materials as prehistory. Prehistoric men left tens of millions of their worked stones on the soil which they inhabited. In many places we need only break the soil to discover bone-heaps and ashes left by early human inhabitants.

Still, prehistory is no more the collecting of stone axes than botany is the gathering of greens. The earth is a marvelous book; unfortunately, time has eaten away at it, and it is written in a language much more difficult than the language of old parchments. But our parchments tell only a small part of the history of our species. To know the rest, our only recourse is to concentrate on the archives of the subsoil and to try to read them.

For a little more than a century students of prehistory have been trying to decipher these archives. Much is known about the distant past of humanity. This knowledge resulted from the exercising of much patience and ingenuity.

FORMATION OF EARTH'S ARCHIVES

The earth's surface is subjected to two opposing influences well known to geologists. On the one hand, rocks are worn

Remains of
the roof of
the cave

Crumbled parts of the roof

The prehistoric
strata are the
pages of the
book of the
earth

Hillside deposits

Bedrock

This is an artist's conception of a beautiful prehistoric site. Under the present-day landscape lies a cave. The cave is not easily recognizable as such because the ceiling has given way for the most part and is now covered by deposits of rubbish from the hillside. The book of the earth is there, protected by thick deposits of rubbish.

away by wind, frost and especially water: the process of *erosion*. On the other hand, the products of erosion are washed away by water and deposited in certain places in successive layers: the process of *sedimentation*.

In this book which encompasses but a few hundreds of thousands of years, we need not be concerned with such geological phenomena as the birth of the mountains or the formation of marine sedimentary strata measuring several feet in depth. These facts belong, not to the history of humanity, but to the history of the earth, which is counted in millions of years. When the first men made their appearance on this planet, the continents and seas were already about the same as today.

But since then, erosion has continued to wear away the mountains. Broken stones torn from the heights have slowly made their way toward the valleys; boulders have turned to pebbles, then gravel, sand and, finally, impalpable clay.

Water is the agent: as it goes from ditch to rivulet, from rivulet to stream, from stream to river, the rain takes up the covering of the landscape, millimeter by millimeter, and carries it to the sea.

If it were possible to set up a camera and take a picture of a landscape every hundred years, the film would show clearly how the movable parts of the soil slide down slopes and disappear into neighboring streams.

The film would also show that the process of displacement is neither continuous nor constant. Erosion grants reprieves to the materials transported: they take this opportunity to fill in cracks and crevices, to level out valleys. One day, they will be taken up again and carried farther. The reprieve may be brief or it may last for centuries, even seem indefinite. *Prehistoric sites* are found in the places where sedimentary strata have been preserved without undue damage. In these privileged spots are registered the archives of the earth.

Let us imagine, for example, a well-protected recess at the base of an overhanging cliff located a short distance from a river. Some men choose to make their home in this shelter. They eat animals, throw away gnawed bones, discard their knicked flint knives, light fires for warmth. After a few years, all visible remains of the hunters are covered by a layer of stones and sediment. The first page has been written. Centuries or thousands of years later, other hunters will notice the same shelter and they in turn will stay there, knowing nothing about their predecessors whose remains are hidden under their feet. They will go away, leaving behind debris characteristic of their mode of living, and soon sediment will cover their debris. The process will continue until a final landslide levels the shelter for all time, closing the cover on the book of the past.

During the same time other men have settled on the banks of streams. Generation after generation, floods have covered with a layer of mud and sand their broken weapons, their lost objects, their discards.

Wherever our ancestors lived, layers of sediment have imprisoned some small part of their history, from the oldest chapters to the most recent. But often erosion has intervened, removing the sediment and carrying away or jumbling everything. The archives of the earth resemble, not a new book, but an old and faded manuscript. Nowhere do we find a complete account of the human adventure from the first to the last line: occasionally separate folios, rarely successive chapters, all of which we must try to fit in among the other remnants of the volume.

PREHISTORIC SITES

In short, a prehistoric site is, among the millions of places where man has lived, one which has to some degree escaped the ravages of time. In proportion to the total surface of the earth, such sites are rare. Not all of them contain the same type of documents.

To understand these documents, look around the house where you are at this moment and imagine that it is abandoned in its present state for several thousand years. Soon the more perishable items will disappear: the cutlet in the cupboard will be but a bone; the draperies will be reduced to a curtainrod and rings. Then the wood of the furniture will rot away; a pile of nails and screws will be all that is left of the cupboard; the bed will be nothing more than a handful of springs. Finally, the whole structure will give way. There will remain only some rubble, broken glass, chipped

What could the student of prehistory learn about this peaceful family of Moï, Indo-China, if the members were trapped in a sudden cataclysm? The diagram of his findings might show the bones of (1) a chicken, (2) a pig, (4) a dog, (3) a child, (6) a woman, (7) a man and two adolescents, and (8) the child's silver necklace. There would be traces of stakes driven into the ground, but the only indication of the lives that they led, the only extant object, is the necklace. If the bones had been dissolved by the soil, as usually happens, this picture of comfortably-equipped peasants would be reduced to the necklace.　　　　　(Plate by Gabille.)

4

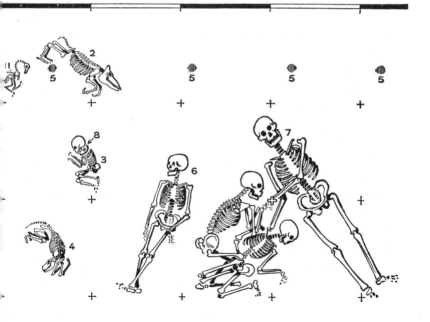

The caves of Saint-Romain (Cote-d'Or). These caves, located some twenty yards above the ground and accessible by a narrow ledge, are a natural fortress in which men sought refuge from Mousterian to Merovingian times, almost without interruption. Unfortunately, this magnificent cave, like many other French stations, has been spoiled by disorderly excavations undertaken in the search for collector's items. (Plate by A. Leroi-Gourhan.)

dishes, rust, and a pile of odd knickknacks which will excite the curiosity of future students of prehistory but which will present many problems if they try to reconstruct the atmosphere of a family evening at home. What were the curtain-rod and copper rings used for? Was it a toy or a social game? And the curious springs—were they ladies' bracelets, the triggering mechanism of a device for shooting projectiles, or trimming for a ceremonial hat?

If you have thought through the problem of the abandoned house, you can now understand prehistory. It is a captivating science, but one that requires caution. The student must use his imagination in reconstructing prehistoric sites but must not make rash statements. He must be able to interpret what he finds.

In recent strata—i.e. going back to the year 2,900 B.C.— are found objects of bone and metal (iron or bronze); pottery; objects of stone, sometimes of wood, rarely of fabrics; quantities of animal bones; and sometimes human sepulchers. The strata which go back eight thousand years B.C. contain the same visible remains except that instead of metal, which was then unknown, one finds worked or polished stones.

Lower down—farther back in time—during the whole age of the reindeer, the list is reduced to bone objects, worked stones, the bones of animals and sometimes of man.

Still farther down, only bones and stones remain.

In the oldest strata, only worked stones have resisted destruction.

From this scant evidence one must try to reconstruct the life of prehistoric man.

There are different types of sites. The most common are those found in the *alluviums* of streams or in the great deposits of silt that cover slopes. Traces of habitations are rarely found there—only stone tools and sometimes bones. These objects were carried along and scattered by erosion, but since periods of erosion alternated with periods of sedimentation, the objects are often arranged in successive strata in the order in which they were deposited; sometimes they were grouped in such a way as to be plentiful at one point and nonexistent elsewhere in the vicinity.

Caves and *overhangs* contain much more valuable sites. A cave is like a box which encloses and protects prehistoric sites. It does not offer absolute protection, for it can not always prevent destruction; but it is often effective and sometimes miraculously so. Unfortunately, caves are restricted to a few regions and many of them have already been pillaged by collectors or careless students. The protection of caves is as important to science as the protection of the manuscripts in libraries. But while no one would think of trying to read a medieval manuscript without knowing Latin, many people imagine they can simply break open the ground and understand what is inside.

Peat-bogs and lakes have the exceptional merit of preserv-

The shelter under Colombière Rock, in l'Ain, is a typical site. The cliff, facing south, provides a wide covert warmed by the sun. The shelter is high enough above the river to be out of danger of floods and at the same time profit by its proximity to the water.
(Plate by Pissot.)

ing wooden objects, leaves and seeds. Our knowledge of the farmers who lived four thousand years ago is due mainly to objects found in peat.

Recent strata near the surface are not, properly speaking, in the province of prehistory. Still, they may contain well-preserved sepulchers, floorings, pottery kilns, and smelting hearths used by prehistoric men. In sites of this type are also found dolmens and menhirs.

There are countless *prehistoric surface sites.* When erosion works gently, it moves the earth toward streams but leaves worked stones along the top of the ground. These are sometimes found scattered in the fields when the land is plowed. These sites have generally preserved nothing except worked stones, and often objects of different periods are mixed together. Thus their contributions to prehistory are of secondary importance; they are like manuscripts that contain only a few scattered legible letters.

A "cleaning" in a Mousterian stratum. The findings are slowly freed by the use of very fine tools and left in the exact spot for later study. Shown here are the remains of the cave-dwelling hyena, the wild horse, and the mammoth.
(Plate by J. Vertut.)

DECIPHERING THE MANUSCRIPT: EXCAVATIONS

Extending the metaphor, to read an old manuscript one must turn slowly through the pages one by one, concentrate on each page and, spending all the time necessary, try to understand the extremely difficult text under examination.

The principle is the same for excavations. One must bare first stratum in its entirety, if possible, *without moving anything*. After having set up the first page of the

9

book of the earth, one must note, photograph, diagram, and try to understand everything exposed. Each grain of soil, each piece of coal, each bit of shapeless rock, is just as important as the most beautiful points of worked flint. Digging into the earth and extracting only the most striking or pleasing objects is equivalent to copying a text and setting down only the nouns, leaving out the articles, pronouns, verbs, and other syntactical accessories. In other words, piecemeal understanding means no understanding at all.

Only after having deciphered the first stratum can one collect the objects uncovered, set aside the samples and specimens necessary for research, and go on to the next layer beneath. All this work requires much time and patience as well as appropriate equipment. To read the book of the earth, one must have more than a pick. An excavation is a veritable dissection of the soil. Generally the student of prehistory, armed with scrapers, pliers and brushes, uncovers the soil over which his ancestors walked, grain by grain.

What is most important is to guard against losing any clue. Diagrams and photographs must make possible the reconstruction of each finding; every relevant particle must be marked and charted. Every useful specimen must be taken up and classified. Here our comparison no longer holds. One can always turn back the pages of a manuscript and concentrate anew on a paragraph already read. But not in the book of the earth. Its pages are destroyed as they are turned. The original text can be read but once; when the earth comprising one stratum is removed, anything which has not been carefully transcribed is irremediably lost.

Each specimen chosen will be studied by a specialist. Man-made objects, like worked stones, are the specialty of the *typologist,* who compares them with previous discoveries. Human bones go to the *anthropologist,* who defines the racial type of the men to whom they belonged. The *paleontologist* studies the bones of animals and helps to determine

10

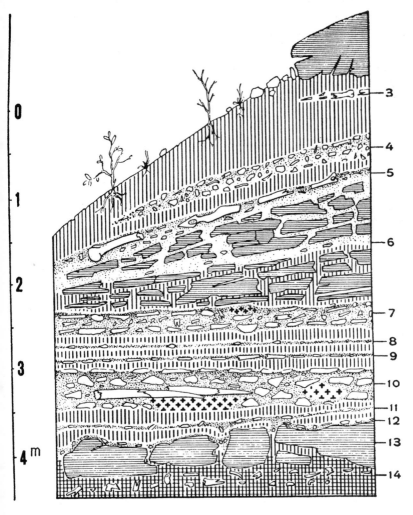

A cross section of the "book of the earth." This diagram of a site shows the progressive crumbling away of the roof of the cavern, the hearths (indicated by crosses), big piles of bone (stratum 5), and the mammoth tusks shown on page 108 (stratum 10).

the climate and the period in which they lived. Large specimens of soil, carefully shielded from contamination, are examined, and fossilized pollens of plants are identified. Larger specimens of soil are given to the *geologist*, who studies them from the point of view of sedimentation and erosion and examines a number of details which give a better understanding of climate and living conditions: he finds particles introduced by the wind or water, signs of glaciation, etc. Fragments of carbonated wood are studied by the *botanist* and the *physicist;* the first identifies the plants used for heat; the second, by measuring its radioactivity, estimates the age of the stratum. By all these methods, one guards against losing a single comma of the prehistoric text. Ultraviolet and infrared rays are used to reveal what the eye can not see under ordinary light. Before finally deciding to take the fatal step and destroy the layer in order to find out what is underneath, one must have done everything possible to preserve the text of this first page of the archives. Moreover, only one part of the site should be excavated; insofar as possible the site is preserved as "evidence" in order that after several years or several centuries have passed, future scholars, with improved techniques and scientific equipment, may again take up the deciphering.

HOW THE TEXT IS USED

Several successive strata have now yielded information about stone tools, animals, plants, climate and men. There is still no written data, and the place of the different parcels of documents in time—the number of years, centuries or millenniums that separate them—is doubtful. Still unknown are the names of the tribes, their chiefs, their gods. There remains no trace of their language, their ideas, their music. The little that has been preserved contributes scant information about even their material life; it is as if one were asked to describe the dress uniform of an imperial grenadier solely from the evidence furnished by one of his pocket buttons.

By way of simplification, let us see how these items, so discouraging at first glance, were used in deciphering the distant past.

It was around the middle of the nineteenth century that serious consideration was first given to the possible significance of worked stones found in the soil. The forerunners of the science of prehistory reasoned in this way: the worked stones must be implements which belonged to men; and since they were buried at a certain depth, they must be very old. Along with the flints were found the bones of the mammoth, the reindeer, and several other animals either extinct or no longer living in the same climate. The conclusion is obvious: in the distant past and under different climatic conditions, man shaped stone implements and weapons.

These first results threw a completely new light on the origin of humanity. They fired the imaginations of scholars during the entire last third of the nineteenth century.

But the second examination of the facts—our own—is more complex. We have at our disposal several parcels of worked stones, each representing a different point in time. Each parcel differs from the preceding. There are several "styles" which apparently were employed successively. Each style has been given a name which generally recalls the geographical location of a prehistoric site. Three parcels, for instance, belong to the following styles:

(1) Acheulean, from Saint-Acheul (Somme);
(2) Solutrean, from Solutre (Saone-et-Loire);
(3) Campignian, from Campigny (Eure).

We also have parcels of the remains of animals from corresponding periods:

(1) Mammoth, Merck rhinoceros, giant deer;
(2) Woolly mammoth, woolly rhinoceros, reindeer;
(3) Stag, castor, pig.

These animals indicate climates roughly as follows:

13

(1) A temperate climate with extinct animals;

(2) A cold climate with animals that are partially extinct;

(3) A temperate climate with semi-domesticated animals.

In addition, the study of fossilized pollens makes it possible to reconstruct for the three parcels the following plants:

(1) Wild vine, box-tree;

(2) Birch, willow;

(3) Oak, beech.

Specimens of soil provided additional information:

(1) What had once been the bank of a stream;

(2) A slope composed of clayey silt and pieces of limestone shivered by frost;

(3) A peaty surface in a woodland setting.

Finally, we have data concerning the men of corresponding or related periods: skeletons, sculptures, and engravings on bones or rocks.

This example shows how we read the texts of our prehistoric archives: by co-ordinating the data of each period, by comparing the periods, and by matching these scraps of truth with corresponding facts in the modern world.

2. CLIMATE AND NATURE

Around the beginning of the last century, the great French naturalist Cuvier studied bones found in the soil and proved that they belonged to extinct species of animals. He went further: starting from a few pieces at his disposal, he succeeded in reconstructing in their entirety these strange beasts. He also showed that they had lived in an environment very different from that of the same regions today.

That is why students of prehistory were already familiar with the idea that nature and climatic conditions had undergone profound changes in the distant past when they first began to build their new science. Scholars began to learn about the great fauna that had disappeared from the earth, i.e. the species that had co-existed during successive periods, and to classify them in their chronological order. What seemed most striking at first was this: the animals that inhabited France during the primary, secondary and tertiary periods had the characteristics of animals living in an almost tropical climate.

When Boucher de Perthes and his disciples showed that men had once lived in France at the beginning of the quaternary at the same time as elephants and rhinoceros, he met with scepticism on the part of the opponents of the new

15

science. They were not surprised to learn that such animals had existed in parts of France since this fact was generally accepted, but they did take issue with the fabulous antiquity which such companions conferred on the human species, which until then had been thought much more recent.

After remains of elephants and worked stone had been found side by side in alluvium deposits, excavations of caves revealed fauna which seemed equally out of place: the reindeer, bison, polar fox, musk ox. France had then experienced in succession an almost tropical climate and a climate similar to that of Lapland. And the idea quickly took root, not only that man had been the contemporary of several large extinct animals, but also that he had spanned great climatic changes.

How were these changes produced? By the beginning of the twentieth century, geologists had shown that the evolution of climatic conditions has been very complicated. Since the beginnings of life on the earth, climatic conditions have undergone important periodic changes, characterized mainly by successive thaws and freezes. At first scholars thought that there had been great climatic variations during the quaternary period (the only period that interests us in our study of the prehistory of man). They finally realized that in regions of the temperate zone where the topography is uneven, such as in France, shifts of less than ten degrees away from the mean annual temperature can change completely the size of glaciers and the distribution of animal and vegetable species.

When the mean temperature rises or falls, the pattern of rainfall is modified. When there is more rain, erosion is accelerated; when there is less rain, it slows down. Modifications in rainfall bring about changes in the rhythm of the process of erosion in such a way that climatic differences will, so to speak, be automatically registered in the layers of sediment. That is why the study of the soil covering prehistoric sites comes first.

STRATA AND THE GLACIAL PERIODS

To understand how the archives of the earth were compiled, one must have a mental picture of the history of a great stream of water, for erosion is the most important force.

Water made its way down mountains and wound its course to the sea. Unless vast shifts of the earth's shell caused changes in the height of mountains and plains, the stream constantly deepened its valley and gradually dropped until it approached sea-level.

When the mean temperature was lowered, glaciers spread out. The Alps, the Pyrenees, the whole of northern Europe were covered by an *ice-cap* like the one that covers Greenland today. This mass of frozen water served to lower the level of the sea several yards. As it fell farther, the stream dug deeper and faster, carving out a valley with steep slopes. But after thousands of years the mean temperature rose. Glaciers melted and receded, the level of the sea rose again. The stream, progressively curbed, ran more slowly and deposited along its course a part of the alluviums that it had formerly carried to the sea. Thus it filled in the lower part of its valley and formed large alluvial plains. When a long cold period set in again, the sea receded, the accelerated descent began anew its rapid digging, and the alluvial plains were like a terrace suspended above the stream. These climatic oscillations were repeated a number of times. The stream continued to make its way down to the sea, depositing on its banks graduated terraces. Each terrace corresponds to a period of warmer climate, to an *interglacial* period. The oldest terraces are at the summit, the most recent at the water's edge.

The glacier, a moving river of ice, in turn registers its alternate advances and withdrawals by abandoning moraine deposits, i.e. masses of rocks and dirt, at its edges.

Finally, the seashore also bears witness to the movements

17

This photograph, taken in 1895, shows a section of the famous gravel-pits of Chelles, near Paris, at the time of the discovery of one of the oldest stages in human history, the Chelean, now called Abbevillean. At the left, behind the man, the strata appear in their normal arrangement. In the center and at the right, they have been shuffled around during the course of glacial periods and show the folds characteristic of rocks moved by thaws in a very cold climate.
(Plate by d'Ault du Mesnil.)

of glaciers: some of the old shores lie above the present coast, others are buried beneath the waters.

Geologists have studied all these layers or strata. They are composed of distinct materials: rough, average or fine; rounded by the sea or striated by the slow progression of the glacier; splintered by frost or polished by the wind. Geologists have tried to understand the subtle orchestration of the climatic changes inscribed in these strata. To decipher these changes is very difficult, for reality is not so simple as our hypothetical scheme. Other phenomena intervened, numerous local accidents jumbled the picture. At one point, the earth slowly rose, causing a hollow in the next period of filling; at another, erosion wiped out an entire episode; or a bend in the river shifted, and the strata reflect only this lateral move and not a change of climate. Finally, since all this evolution occurred before recorded history began, there is nothing to prove whether or not sections of a certain region correspond to the same span of time as sections of another.

The result is that scholars are still not agreed on the exact number of glacial periods and minor secondary climatic fluctuations. The prevalent opinion is that there must have been four great periods during which glaciers covered a large part of the surface of the continents. These four successive glaciations have been given the names of the four small affluents of the Danube, where vestiges of them were first studied: Günz, Mindel, Riss and Würm. The formation of the banks of streams has been compared with the structure of seashores with a view to setting up a correspondence between shores and banks, both of which must have resulted from the same climatic fluctuations. These comparisons are problematical for the oldest glaciations, Günz and Mindel. They are more certain in the case of Riss. For Würm, they are fairly well established. The most important steps in the evolution of man seem to have been taken during the Riss glaciation, the interglacial Riss-Würm period, and finally, the Würm glaciation, which was followed by the present period of temperate climate.

EVIDENCE FURNISHED BY PLANTS

Microscopic grains of pollen are able miraculously to resist destructive forces. They can, under ideal conditions (such as in peaty soil), survive unchanged for tens of thousands of years. Each year billions and billions of these tiny grains are broken open and their impalpable dust is scattered by the winds. By examining these particles under a microscope, the botanist can easily identify the plant from which they came. The grains of pollen are almost certain to show the type of climate that existed at the time they were deposited in a layer of soil. Indeed, the life of each species of wild plant is closely linked to the climate favorable to this species; unlike animals, plants cannot flee from the cold in

19

winter and change from one place to another in accordance with the seasons. One need only be familiar with the successive species of plants of a particular region in order to reconstruct with certainty the climatic variations of this region.

The botanist chooses a suitable section of a site and gathers small samples (five centimeters square and five deep, for example), taking care not to introduce any present-day pollens. With the microscope, he is able to determine for each sample the exact proportion of pines with respect to birch or hazel. By examining successive strata, he can see clearly how one of these species disappeared or, on the contrary, won out over the others.

The different groupings of plants found in each stratum reveal more than climatic changes. They also show the character of corresponding landscapes: here the damp forest, there steppes, elsewhere prairies interspersed with woodlands.

Geology and botany, each of which complements the findings of the other, thus provide the means for accurately reconstructing, in the sites which lend themselves to this type of research, the lives of men and animals of prehistoric times.

Study of the plants of the quaternary period soon indicated that, except for a few points which were really very cold, the climate was not marked by such extreme variations as earlier scholars had supposed on discovering that the same regions had been inhabited successively by reindeer and elephants. The mean temperature at Orleans during the glacial periods, for example, was approximately the same as the mean temperature of Copenhagen today; and during the warmest of the interglacial periods, the mean temperature probably was no higher than that of Seville today. But the import of this type of comparison is limited by the fact that, though the mean temperature of a region varied, its latitude always remained constant; following the example given, the sun has always risen higher in the Orleans sky than at Copenhagen. In many regions climatic differences linked to variations of temperature must have been less pronounced than comparisons with present-day geography would indicate. Against this, when glaciers descended into the valleys, the neighboring regions evidently were subjected to intense cold. The topography of France indicates the intensity of the cold during the glacial periods. It is hard to imagine just how severely the temperature had to drop in order to produce, even when the sun shone brightly in the summertime, the huge masses of ice which advanced as far as the banks of the Rhone.

During the great freezes of the Würm glaciation, which we understand a little better than the others, France must have had a very complicated botanical pattern. Alpine plants extended down into the low plains, and vast expanses of the cold steppe covered whole regions. But the plants of the interglacial period, similar to modern plants, continued to cling to the soil in the regions far from the glacier. The situation with respect to animal species was the same: at times the chamois lived side by side in France with the reindeer and the wild horse.

THE ANIMALS

We know only the broad outlines of the distribution of animal species for the periods preceding the Würm glaciation. From that time on, however, it is possible to picture their distribution with relative precision. We know which game prehistoric men hunted and which species, among these animals, were more abundant. We even have pictorial evidence of some of their hunts, such as the famous aurochs of the Lascaux cave.

On examining different geological layers, one finds no exact correspondence, especially for the beginnings of the quaternary period, between the succession of climatic periods and animal species. The animals which were adapted to a

During the greater part of the quaternary, the main game animals were not reindeer but wild horses and aurochs. In the Lascaux cave prehistoric man painted most extraordinary figures of aurochs, the direct ancestors of some of our domestic cattle. (Plate by Archives photographiques.)

warm climate at the beginning of the quaternary apparently were progressively supplanted by "colder" and "colder" animals, the "coldest" appearing at the end of the Würm glaciation and being supplanted in turn by present-day animals. At the end of the tertiary period, Europe had a great variety of animals. The regions of France, though lacking a tropical climate, had every appearance of zoological gardens, rivaling the African savannahs of a hundred years ago. The plains and streams of France were the home of herds of mastodons, wild horses, zebras and hippopotamuses. Roe deer of great size, bears, rhinoceros, saber-toothed tigers, and giant castors reclined in the shade of oaks and walnut trees. The period which geologists classify as the beginning of the quaternary changed the picture but slightly: the big-toothed tigers and mastodons disappeared while elephants multiplied and the other species continued to flourish.

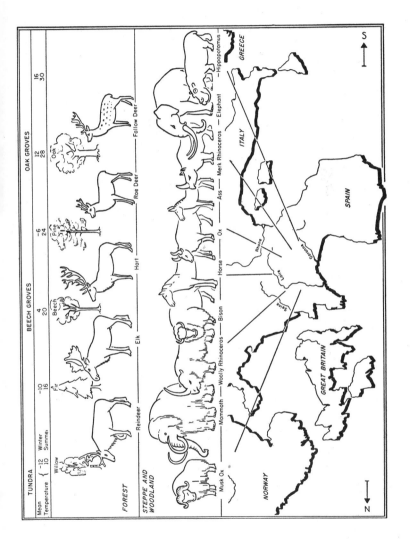

The diagram shows, for southwestern France, the different animals characteristic of different climates, from the reindeer and the musk ox, which now live
in the Arctic, to the hippopotamus.

Thus France, which had a climate not too different from that of today, was inhabited by fauna typical of modern Africa, including hippopotamuses and rhinoceros. This may seem surprising at first, but these animals are really no more typical of Africa than of Europe. What has happened is simply that they have survived in Africa whereas they disappeared from Europe, and this for two reasons. First, climatic changes in Africa fluctuated from tropical to equatorial; between the two extremes there was not enough difference to deal the death blow to the larger animals. The difference between the temperate and cold glacial periods, though probably little greater, was enough to wipe out many animals in Europe. Second, in Europe man, the hunter, made his presence felt almost everywhere while in Africa he left large expanses untouched. Proof of the ravages wrought by man on the animal species is that only a few centuries ago, under climatic conditions similar to those of France, there were still lions, rhinoceros and tapirs in Asia. They became extinct relatively recently, not because of natural conditions, but because of man. And in central Asia, in Siberia, where the winters are much more severe than in France, there are still tigers and panthers.

After the Riss glaciation come the periods which furnish the greatest amount of information about prehistoric man. By this time the great castors, the saber-toothed tigers and the hippopotamuses had long since disappeared from the scene of history. What game did our distant ancestors hunt? We can get an idea by picturing to ourselves western Europe as it was during the period that separated the Riss glaciation from the Würm glaciation, at a time when the climate was similar to the present-day climate and the same plants were growing in the same regions.

Far to the north, toward Scandinavia and northern Russia, lay the *tundra,* and *marshlands,* swampy forests of elms, willows and pines. Through them roamed mammoths, reindeer and musk oxen. Packs of wolves and wolverines lived at the expense of these larger animals and smaller prey as well: lemmings (similar to field mice), white rabbits and part-ridges. The smaller animals were also the usual victims of the blue fox and the snow owl. Except for the mammoth, all these animals still exist today in Siberia or in Canada.

South of this region began the great forests of resinous and leafy trees. The resinous trees were the domain of elks, martens and small gray squirrels; the leafy forest sheltered deer, bison and some woolly rhinoceros. Woolly rhinoceros and mammoths apparently roamed also between the tundra and the forest.

Farther to the south, the landscape was different. In western Europe the leafy forest continued, broken by ex-panses of treeless terrain, but in central Europe began the great steppes that extended to northern China. Through the woods and plains roved herds of wild cattle and horses, joined farther to the north by mammoths, woolly rhinoceros, and some reindeer. On the cold steppes lived the *saiga* (a sheep-like antelope) and a small rodent, the ground squirrel.

During the interglaciary period France was divided into forests, plains and mountains, and was covered by plants similar to those of today. In the forests lived harts, red deer, roe deer, and wild boars; in the plains, wild horses and cattle, large mammoths and Merck rhinoceros, more closely related to the modern rhinoceros than the woolly rhinoceros. In the south were wild asses. Wild goats and chamois and marmots lived in the mountains. The last hippopotamuses probably survived in the extreme south of France.

All these herbivores were chased by numerous carnivores: wolves smaller than those of the north, wild dogs, lions, panthers and, in the forests, lynxes. Brown bears, similar to modern brown bears, were numerous, as were cave bears, which are now extinct. The cave bears varied greatly in size. Some were scarcely larger than a great Dane while the giants of the species could stand on their hind legs and sniff an object more than a dozen feet from the ground. The

The animal most often hunted throughout prehistoric times was the wild horse. There existed many races adapted to as many different climates; during temperate periods as well as during the heaviest freezes, horses lived in almost every region.

cave bears, which were probably not very carnivorously inclined, lived communally in the mountains and withdrew into the caves to hibernate.

To summarize, the animals of the period that separated the Riss and Würm glaciations lived under climatic conditions similar to those of today. They included:

(1) Polar fauna, notably reindeer, mammoths, musk oxen;

(2) Fauna of the forest and northern steppe—elks, mammoths, woolly rhinoceros, bisons;

(3) Fauna of the temperate forests and steppes—horses, cattle, harts, red deer;

(4) Toward the Mediterranean, the same animals plus woolly mammoths, Merck rhinoceros, deer and asses.

Though more than a hundred thousand years have passed since then, most of these species still exist. The only ones now extinct are the mammoth, the rhinoceros, and the cave bear. Man is probably responsible for their disappearance; these big animals were an easy target for the hunters whose numbers constantly increased and whose weapons became progressively more effective.

As for the small mammals—field mice, ground squirrels, gray squirrels, foxes and badgers—most of them have survived, along with countless species of birds, ranging from the eagle to the vulture and wren. The giant penguin was exterminated only a century ago.

This does not mean that every animal was exactly like its modern descendant. In a thousand centuries lions, horses, and reindeer have evolved, but so little that one might hesitate a moment before deciding which is the more recent when confronted with an aurochs of the pre-Würm glaciation period and a modern Spanish bull.

The climatic variations during the quaternary were less severe than scholars had first assumed on discovering traces of glacial periods (see page 16). Still, they determined movements in the redistribution of plant species, and these movements resulted in migrations of animals. When certain plants moved toward the north or toward the south, they were followed by the animals which fed on them. If we had been granted a prolonged existence and had remained seated on the banks of the Loire from the end of the Riss glaciation until the end of the Würm glaciation, we might have observed in their northward migration, first the reindeer and mammoths, then the elks, then the horses and cattle, and finally, the giant deer and mammoths. After some climatic fluctuations and the sudden freeze that marked the beginning of the Würm glaciation, we would have seen these animals retreat toward the south and the reindeer again roam for centuries along the banks of the Loire. Scarcely ten thousand years before the recent period, after the Würm glaciation had ended, we would have witnessed another great migration to the north. But when the harts, cattle and horses reappeared on the Loire, they were not accompanied by the great representatives of the extinct fauna, mammoths and rhinoceros. Moreover, horses and cattle were nearing the stage of domestication, when man would

Though the reindeer did not live continuously in France throughout prehistoric times, great herds returned each time the climate became colder.

take them from the plains and lead them to the stable and stall.

WHAT THE PAST WAS ACTUALLY LIKE

Students of prehistory have patiently assembled thousands of details about the distant past of the human species. They have studied the pebbles and sands of streams, and the clay of caves. They have examined the imprints of plants and pollens and of the smallest tooth of the smallest animal. One by one they have counted and mapped the thin sheets of clay left by successive glaciers. By furnishing these results, their science, which at first seemed almost impossible, has now given us the true picture of our past.

What do we know about the distant past of the human species?

First, that this past embraces an almost astronomical span of time: a hundred thousand years, two hundred thousand, five hundred thousand. A more exact date can not be assigned, but a variation of two or three hundred thousand years leaves unchanged the marvel of the spectacular scope of the human adventure.

We also know that the remote ancestors of the French lived among elephants and reindeer. But these elephants never saw bananas; they fed on the leaves and twigs of oaks. Nor did reindeer experience the long polar night. The contrasts of climate were not great. An annual lowering of the mean temperature of ten or twelve degrees was enough to cause the elephants to give way to the mammoths, the oak forests to retreat to Italy and Spain, and the glacier on Mont Blanc to block the Saône near Lyons.

Students of prehistory are not so certain about the beginnings of the quaternary; they know little about the succession of climates or of animal species. But from the Riss glaciation on, the picture becomes clearer. Except for a few mammals, every animal that existed then is still found somewhere in the zone bounded by the Arctic Circle and the latitude of Algeria. During the period that separated the Riss and Würm glaciations, the species that lived in France were the same as those now found in the southern half of this zone; during the Würm glaciation, the species were those now found in the northern half. In reality, however, the division was not so precise. There were, according to the region, different mixtures of the two groups of animals. One must also allow for the differences of latitude in France: the last extinct elephants may have lived along the Côte-d'Azur just when waves of mammoths and reindeer were invading northern France.

Our prehistoric setting is now complete. The time has come for the entrance of the protagonist: man.

3. PREHISTORIC MAN

Skeletal remains of prehistoric animals are rare: often half a molar will be the only sign of a herd of elephants. Men were fewer in number than elephants, and their skeletons are more fragile. The whole collection of human traces discovered throughout Europe during a century of research takes up very little space. By careful packing, one could place in a week-end kit all the remains antedating the Würm glaciation. For the period that separated the Riss and Würm glaciations, an officer's canteen would be ample. A suitcase would be required for the first part of the Würm glaciation, and three or four trunks for the second. Furthermore, the remains that are uncovered are never complete. If we have the good fortune to come upon a jawbone, the whole cranium is missing; if by chance we find a cranial cap, the front is missing. For the period antedating the Riss glaciation, there is not a single skull which can be reconstructed in its entirety. Up until the Würm glaciation, there is no skeleton to accompany the three or four almost complete craniums in our possession. The Würm glaciation is more generous: we actually have some skeletons which are almost complete.

This material, though restricted, is eloquent. By studying it carefully, scholars have succeeded in sketching—with broad strokes, at any rate—the portrait of the first men.

Early discoveries made our ancestors appear as creatures with low foreheads and jutting snoots, very close to beasts. Heated controversies arose over these remains. Some looked upon man as an ape that had climbed to the top rung of the zoological ladder; others thought that these poor low-browed creatures were not quite men and that our true ancestors remained to be discovered. The discussion took the form of an attack on or a defense of religion; to the voices of those who really understood the evidence were added others, less competent, and this weighed against considering the problem of the origin of man with the necessary calmness and clarity.

With the discovery in the Rhine valley of the first remains of Neanderthal man, with his low forehead and protruding sockets, scholars imagined that they had found the perfect link between the gorilla and modern man. But as one discovery followed another, the intermediate place was attributed to the Pithecanthrope and, more recently, to the Australopithecan. There have been found beings older than Neanderthal man, yet closer to modern man! And even the poor Neanderthal man was more intelligent than his flat cranium suggests. The result of all these discoveries is that scholars now suppose that in the distant past, several types of men co-existed on the earth much as they do today, but with more pronounced differences.

THE GENERAL OUTLINES OF ZOOLOGICAL EVOLUTION

During the primary period certain vertebrates freed themselves from the original marine element and acquired lungs which allowed them to breath in the air. They reached solid ground and became quadrupeds. The transitional forms are not known, but still today there are numerous fish which can assimilate oxygen from the air and spend long hours outside the liquid element, making their way from one marsh to the next during dry seasons.

These first inhabitants of the land divided into two branches, the amphibians or bactracians and the reptiles. The secondary period was the age of great reptiles like the Brontosaurus and the Diplodocus; but even these well-known giants did not match the modern whale in size. Alongside these monsters, during the latter half of the secondary period, lived other smaller reptiles the size of rats or dogs. Their limbs had grown longer, and some of them had hair and probably a warm-blooded circulatory system; they had developed incisors, canines and molars. In short, their biological features and general appearance linked them closely to primitive mammals. From this group of reptiles issued, toward the end of the secondary period, the first real mammals, which were to dominate the earth during the whole tertiary period.

These primitive mammals, small and not well developed at first, began at the outset of the tertiary period to evolve in the direction of modern groups like the herbivores and carnivores. Certain genealogical lines seemed to move by steps toward horses and ruminants; others became felines or hyenas. These trends are revealed when, starting from existing species, we go back in time. The ancestor of the horse was apparently the animal which most closely resembled him, during a certain period, in the manner in which he was adapted to running and feeding. Adaptation, which has several explanations, is an indisputable fact. A mammal that lived during the first part of the tertiary period and tended to live and eat (non-ruminant herbivore frequenting the great open steppe) in the manner of future horses, would normally evolve according to the modern formula for a horse. An astounding fact is this: the multiple conditions necessary for the development of horses appeared at least twice in two different strains of animals: horses proper and a strange South American mammal, the *Thoaterium* which, after having issued from a distinct source and developed almost every feature of the horse, became extinct.

The last example is priceless. It throws light on one of the difficulties of the problem of man's origin. Among the fossilized remains of animals that tended toward the attainment of humanity, it is hard to distinguish between those that actually succeeded and those that may have followed parallel routes without having reached the status of human beings.

Among the primitive mammals that evolved continuously toward modern species are the first representatives of the *primates*. At the beginning of the tertiary period they still closely resembled all their congeners. Like the others, they had an undifferentiated tooth structure adapted to their varied diet of fruits, sprouts and insects; like them they had five digits on each limb, a very small body, and a skeleton adapted specifically to neither a mobile life on the plains nor a life restricted to the trees.

But the other strains evolved through differentiation in divergent directions. Their teeth became instruments for gnawing, for cropping grass, for grinding grain, or for cutting meat. Their limbs were adapted to swift running and jumping; their digits were reduced in number and fused to produce the hoofs of modern horses, cattle and hogs.

Only the primates remained abnormally stationary, undergoing little evolution with respect to these basic traits. Their apparent stagnation is one of the most salient traits of their nature. All of them, including man, have preserved the possibility of eating everything, of moving their limbs in all directions, of making use of their twenty digits, and of sitting or standing with the trunk erect. All of this is the result of the distinctive evolution of primates: the increase in the size of the brain. Because of this brain, they made the best possible use of a body not perfectly adapted to any one specific function but capable of exercising all.

Not all primates followed the evolutionary route with

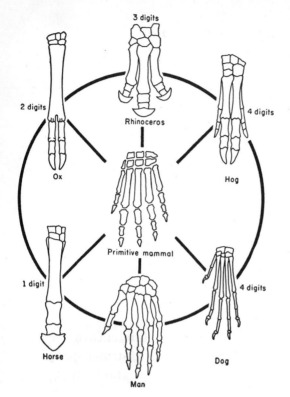

In the center, the hand of an early tertiary mammal. Around it are arranged the front feet of modern mammals, showing progressive specialization for walking, from the dog with his five digits (one of which is useless), to the four-digited hog, the three-digited rhinoceros, the two-digited ox, and finally, the horse with but one effective digit. Below, the human hand which, though strangely conservative in that it closely resembles that of primitive mammals and certain reptiles of the primary period, has refined and perfected all its articulations to the extent of becoming the faithful servant of the brain.

equal success. Still today there are examples of different formulas, from the small-brained lemurs to chimpanzees. But toward the middle of the tertiary period appeared the first representatives of a great group which was to found a superior class of primates, the Anthropoids, Australopithecans, and Anthropes.

The Anthropoids probably correspond to the first of several branches which terminated with the modern gorilla, chimpanzee, orangutan and gibbon. Though they all evidence considerable development of the brain, they still retain (at least in the case of the forms that have been studied up to this time) a semi-quadruped appearance and numerous traits of true monkeys.

34

About twenty years ago, the remains of an extraordinary group of primates were discovered in Africa: the Australopithecans. Several craniums have been discovered, and the skeletal structure of these primates is well known. Not only was their brain better developed proportionately than that of the Anthropoids, but also their dental structure was almost identical to that of man; they had small canines and were unique among the primates in that they walked erect, like man. The exact period during which they lived is unknown, and nothing proves that they were really the ancestors of man; but they evidence, at a very primitive stage, the association of three characteristics which they alone share with man: a relatively generalized dental structure, non-jutting facial features, and upright walk.

THE ANTHROPES: MEN OR GORILLAS?

Anthropes include all fossil primates who not only walked upright and had well-developed brains but also left indisputable evidence of their ability to fabricate implements; all apparently had the mental capacity to transmit their skills from generation to generation. The production of implements assumes in effect, as we shall soon see, the preservation of a technical heritage, and this is distinct from the pattern of life of lower animals.

Anthropes fall into three groups: the Archanthropes, the Paleanthropes and the Neanthropes. Their succession in time is not clear. The periods during which they lived on the earth even overlap.

VERY OLD MEMBERS OF THE FAMILY OF MAN: THE ARCHANTHROPES

Traces of the Archanthropes were discovered in Java (Pithecanthrope), in the region of Peking (Sinanthrope) and quite recently in Palikao, Algeria (Atlanthrope). These

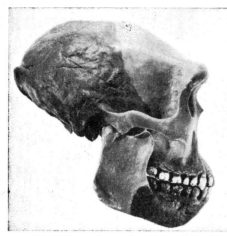

The Pithecanthrope (profile) and the Sinanthrope (three-quarter view) as they have been reconstructed from numerous fragments. Both are closely related and are much nearer to man than to monkeys.

creatures have often been called pre-human, but they are more aptly designated as archanthropes, which means "very old members of the human family." For it is difficult to determine where humanity begins, and we do not know enough about these creatures to say whether they were human or pre-human. They were acquainted with the use of fire, and they shaped instruments. Their skulls were about twice the size of the skull of a gorilla but smaller than ours. Their teeth and facial features were also half-way between those of the gorilla and ours. Perhaps the Archanthropes marked one of the first steps in the evolution of primates. Or perhaps they had nothing to do with our ascendancy. In any event, they point up (as did the Australopithecans) the extraordinary surge of the primates toward higher forms of life.

THE LAST PRIMITIVES: THE PALEANTHROPES

From Java, China and Algeria, we return to Europe: though no Archanthropes have been discovered there, traces of Paleanthropes are numerous. And there is no question as to whether the Paleanthropes were men or super-gorillas.

36

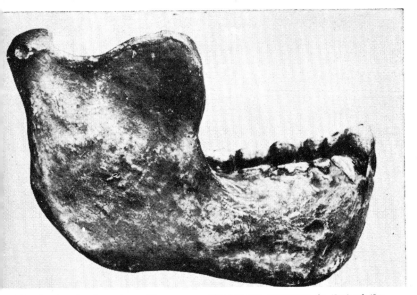

The famous jawbone from Mauer, near Heidelberg, Germany, is that of the oldest known man. Unfortunately, all that remains of the Heidelberg man is this jawbone; during the fifty years since its discovery, nothing else of similar age or appearance has been found. Because it is of the same age as the oldest worked stones of Europe, and because the teeth resemble those of Neanderthal man, everyone agrees that the jawbone belonged to a man.
(Plate by Musée de l'Homme.)

They were definitely men, and their works evidence a fully human capacity for technical creativity.

Scarcely fifty years ago, our only information about the Paleanthropes was the famous Neanderthal man. But more recently other traces have been discovered, and we now know that these old representatives of the human species included members from distinct races.

The oldest trace of the Paleanthropes is the jawbone found at Mauer, near Heidelberg, Germany. The man to whom it belonged was the contemporary of the last hippopotamuses. He had a huge mandible, no chin, and big teeth similar in other respects to our own. He probably resembled very closely the man whose paintings adorn the caves of France (see page 57).

Next come two fossils that antedate the Riss glaciation, one found in England and the other in France. Unfortunately, they are no more than cranial caps. The first is from

37

Swanscombe, the second from Fontechevade. Their general appearance is the same: though thick, they are similar in shape to ours. In all probability, long before the Neanderthal men there were skulls that enclosed brains fairly similar to those of modern men.

Then comes a skull found at Steinheim, Germany, which may date from the Riss glaciation. It offers a strange blending of primitive and modern features. The occiput is rather modern; the frontal bone is that of Neanderthal man; the facial bones have features of both types of men.

Last on the list come two skulls, one from Saccopastore, Italy, and the other from Gibraltar. They are fairly complete but lack the lower jaw. They correspond almost perfectly to the fossils found in the Arcy cave—to Augustine's companions. The latter, in turn, are complete except for the cranial cap. We know that all these men were small and had brains larger than those of the Sinanthropes but still smaller than those of modern men. They had low, slanted foreheads and protruding eye-sockets. Their faces, though not prominent, were long and strong. Their big teeth were better adapted to grinding and chewing than to tearing flesh. The lower jaw was enormous, and the whole masticat-

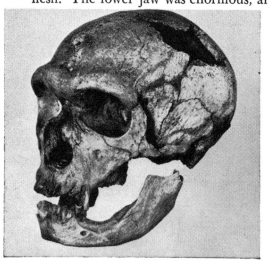

The skull from La Chapelle-aux-Saintes, France (from the collection of the Musée de l'Homme), is the best preserved of the five known skulls of Neanderthal men. The others are those from La Ferrassie, La Quina and Le Moustier (France) and Circe, Italy. (See map, page 40).

Plate by Petite Documentation francaise.)

ing apparatus was not rivaled in strength by any except that of the Heidelberg man. All these remains date from the period that separated the Riss and Würm glaciations, or from the beginning of the Würm glaciation. Several skulls from the same period have been found in Palestine, but they represent larger men, closer in appearance to modern men; they differ but little from those of modern indigenous Australians.

NEANDERTHAL MAN

Many traces of Paleanthropes of the Neanderthal type have been found in caves. At the beginning of the Würm glaciation, the cold, damp climate forced men to seek refuge in natural caves, wherever these could be found; when there were no caves, men probably built huts, though no trace of such efforts on the part of the Paleanthropes has yet been found.

Bones of Neanderthal men have been uncovered almost everywhere in Europe. The three best findings were in France, at La Chapelle-aux-Saintes, La Ferrassie and La Quina. They include complete craniums and most of the skeletons. Our knowledge of the Paleanthropes that antedated the Würm glaciation is limited, but we have detailed information about the physical appearance of Neanderthal men.

Of average stature, they displayed great variety according to regions and periods. Some retained a stooped posture, the last sign of their affiliation with other vertebrates; others stood perfectly erect. Their brains (which have been partially reconstructed by moldings taken from the cranial cavities) were slightly different from ours but at least as large. The top of Neanderthal man's skull was low and his eyesockets were enormous, as in the case of the preceding Paleanthropes. The face, too, was probably similar in appearance to ours but less elongated and much larger.

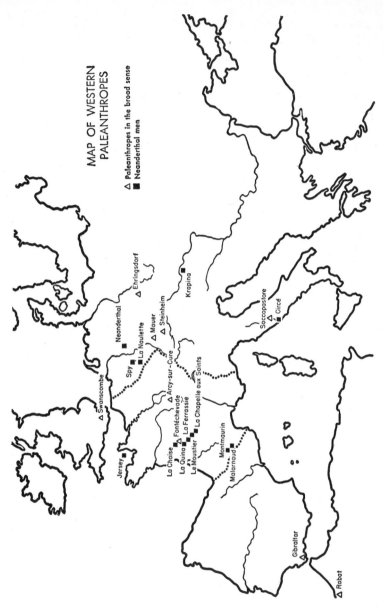

MAP OF WESTERN
PALEANTHROPES

△ Paleanthropes in the broad sense
■ Neanderthal men

Swanscombe
Neanderthal
Spy
La Naulette
Ehringsdorf
Mauer
Steinheim
Krapina
Arcy-sur-Cure
La Chapelle aux Saints
Fontéchevade
La Ferrassie
Jersey
La Chaise
La Quina
Le Moustier
Montmaurin
Malarnaud
Soccopastore
Circé
Gibraltar
Rabat

Map of the main discoveries of Paleanthropes, showing that the traces are not uniformly distributed. In northern Germany and England as in the great mountainous regions, one can scarcely expect to find them; climatic conditions there were probably not favorable to settlement. In the other regions limestone caves protected bones. Considering both the favorable and the unfavorable conditions, it is obvious that fairly large numbers of Paleanthropes occupied most of western Europe.

The forearms and legs were stubby, the hands and feet short and wide. Imprints left in the clay of a cave by Neanderthal men have recently been found in Italy.

We know a little more about the way of life of the Neanderthal men than of their predecessors. Those who lived in caves apparently were not overly concerned with comfort. Still, in the Arcy cave where the author works, the strata above Augustine indicate continuous progress toward cleanliness; the middle part of the cave was well kept, free from trash and garbage, but lined with flint implements and pieces of worked bone. Their stock of implements were generally well cared for and not inferior to the tools of their successors, the Neanthropes. They knew how to butcher animals: their flint knives left marks on very wisely chosen points; the marks show, for example, where Neanderthal men cut the hide of the reindeer in order to skin the animal and where they sliced the tendons in order to dismember the bear.

Study of the way of life of the last Neanderthal men who lived in France makes it increasingly more difficult to look upon them as the link between man and the ape, as some have done. The men found at La Chapelle-aux-Saintes and La Ferrassie were interred by their peers, which probably indicates their concern for religion. There have also been found, in the caves of the Neanderthal men, pieces of red ocher, fossil shells and peculiarly-shaped stones. The tendency to collect curiosities is the first step in developing an artistic sense.

The intellectual level of Neanderthal man was probably higher than the shape of his skull would suggest. During the last part of their stay in western Europe, they must have become acquainted with their successors, the Neanthropes. This contact must have lasted for centuries. In contrast to the Neanthropes, the last Neanderthal men must have lived as an inferior race, crouched or even cooped in their caves. They may have copied from their superiors certain accom-

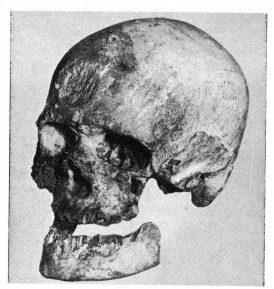

The skull of the famous "Old-man Cro-Magnon" of Dordogne, France (Musée de l'Homme collection). Though toothless, he is really not so old—probably not more than fifty thousand. In his cave, he was covered by a crust of tarnished calcite and lost a large portion of his mandible. But he is still at the head of the line of the Cro-Magnon sculptors and painters of the age of the reindeer, and he is so like us that only experts can tell the difference.
(Plate by Petite Documentation française.)

plishments like sepulchers, implements and artistic activities; yet this single fact—their being able to imitate—is a clear sign of their mental possibilities and aptitudes.

OUR FELLOW-CREATURES: THE NEANTHROPES

One day there appeared other men, men similar to us. Where did they come from? No one knows. On their arrival the climate, which had been mild for some time, became cooler, then bitter cold set in and there was no relief for centuries. The Neanderthal men had hunted the ox and the horse much more than the reindeer. The early Neanthropes were first and foremost hunters of reindeer; hence the name given their period, the *age of the reindeer*. This age lasted for several thousand years. Each region was probably peopled by a specific type, somewhat as today. Four main races of the age of the reindeer have been identified and named after the first four distinct skeletons brought to light. The most famous is the Cro-Magnon, big, short-faced and long-skulled, little different from certain modern Euro-

42

peans; the remains of this race are found in southwestern France. At about the same time, men of the Grimaldi race were living in southeastern France. Two skeletons found in the vicinity of Menton link the Grimaldi men to certain African Negroes. The Combe-Capelle race is named for a skeleton found in Dordogne. A little later came the Chancelade race; skeletal remains were found at Chancelade and Charente. Other skeletons, not linked to any definite group, have also been discovered.

All these men belong, like us, to the species *Homo sapiens.* Their brains were large, their teeth and faces small; their backbones were adapted to an upright position. From the viewpoint of their intellect, no distinction between them and us can be drawn. The level of their technical knowledge, attested by their industry, was the same as that found today among the most advanced tribes dependent for their subsistence on hunting and fishing. Their artistic activities, known through thousands of objects, paintings, engravings and sculptures found in caves, reveal artistic mastery and religious preoccupations which link them closely to modern man.

After the last glaciation ended, other men reached France and prepared the setting for the people of the historical period. They were still Neanthropes. After them, excavations reveal no traces of men less suited than we for modern living. Their task was accomplished.

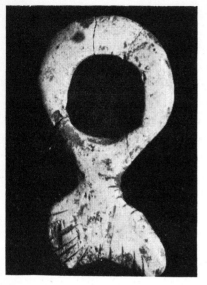

This carved bone object dates from the middle of the first period of the age of the reindeer (Perigordian II). It is one of the oldest known "gems," antedating the Magdalenian sculptures by several thousand years. Its abstract shape gives no clue to its use and signification, though its owner presumably attributed to it magical properties. It comes from stratum 7 of the Arcy cave (see page 11).
(Plate by P. Poulain.)

4. THE WORKS OF PREHISTORIC MAN

We now know that the span of man's existence is immense, that it embraces several geological periods and several changes of climate and fauna. We know that during each period there existed human beings very different from ourselves. We do not know whether there were in Europe Archanthropes similar to the Pithecanthropes and Sinanthropes, but we know that the Paleanthropes were many and varied, some fairly closely linked to modern man, others (especially the Neanderthal men) a backward step in the evolution of *Homo sapiens*. Finally, we know that *Homo sapiens* appeared in France while the last mammoths were still living there.

Here we begin to study all these men, not from the viewpoint of the shape of their skulls, but from the viewpoint of their works. Because the creation of technics is one of the most distinctive characteristics of man, we could find no better guide.

What is most astounding is that the creations of prehistoric man transcend time, race, and creative type. It is possible to

44

write the complete history of human technics without having to study the history of skeletons: whether ape-like or a genius, the first worker, starting from zero, had to limit himself to the simple act of breaking a stone in two and forming thereby a cutting instrument. His distant successor hundreds of thousands of years later, even if mentally inferior, could not ignore all that had been discovered before him; he would of necessity profit by it. Immaterial creations like songs, rites and social or religious principles may die out or be given new life from one period to another; but the tool summarizes and prolongs the thought of every preceding generation. Each generation is heir to a solid technical basis on which it may subsist without advancement if lacking in imagination, but which will be enriched if the slightest spark of creative intelligence adds something new.

To describe completely the civilizations which succeeded each other during the quaternary period, one would need an overall view of:

(1) Man's means of subsistence (hunting, fishing, gathering plant foods);

(2) His means of protection (clothing, habitation);

(3) The organization of his society;

(4) His religious and artistic pursuits.

It is often difficult, even in the case of ancient cultures that left written evidence, to draw up a complete account of a civilization. But prehistoric documents alone give abundant data.

Some furnish direct evidence: thus from the manner in which they worked flint, it is possible to learn the degree of technical development attained by the men who lived during a specific period. The others contribute indirect evidence: for instance, when an engraving of a bison wounded by a spear is found hidden in a remote corner of an almost inaccessible cave, it is probable that the artist who created it did not choose such a place solely in order to be able to

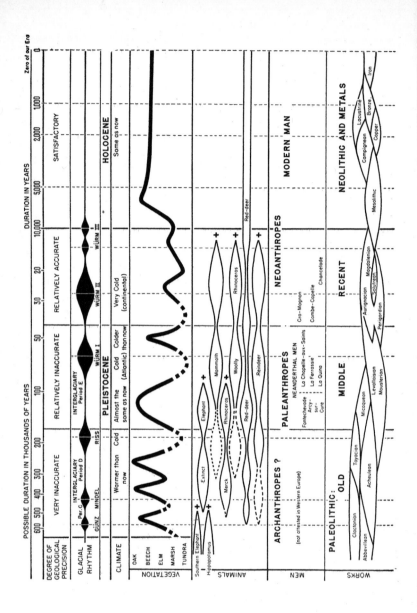

This table summarizes the findings of prehistoric anthropology. The logarithmic scale is used because of limitations of space. Thus the Acheulean period, apparently the same as the Mesolithic, was actually a hundred times as long.

work in peace; he sought after the mysterious, and this is an indication of religious or magical thought.

Apart from the indications that they give about the technical level of a culture, direct documents do not always furnish much information. It may be possible to reconstruct the process of fabrication by studying a flint point, but that does not reveal its function. Here astute hypotheses are introduced. Was the piece of flint a knife? Or, more probably, the point of a spear? Or a piercer? A student of prehistory will never say anything like this: "The point was used by women to cut from the hide of an eighteen-month-old male musk ox thongs for the vamps of the moccasins which men wore while trapping partridges on the snow in the spring. . . ." To be sure, we have little better knowledge of certain objects that date from Roman antiquity or the middle ages, even though we know their names from texts.

The preceding statements do not imply that students of prehistory must appeal to their imagination in order to reconstruct the mode of life of our remote ancestors. Happily, indirect evidence is sufficiently expressive to allow valid interpretations. Here are some examples:

A human skeleton lying on a layer of powdered red ochre, which is not an uncommon finding, is surely an indication of some religious rite.

Pierced shells suggest that ornamentation played a certain role but leave unspecified their specific function—as necklaces, bracelets, trimmings for clothing or charms.

Odd-shaped stones found besides shells, bits of ore, and samples of rock crystal indicate that men gathered them because they thought them beautiful and attributed to them magical powers. This dual concern is generally observed among modern tribes who make similar collections.

Finally, the failure of any prehistoric tribe to engage in agriculture points to the conclusion that for long periods there were no cities or even aggregations comprising hundreds of individuals. Men who depended for their livelihood solely on hunting and fishing could exist only in small groups. Each year a dozen or more reindeer were needed to feed one man. The maximum distance from which slaughtered animals could be transported to their homes was probably about a dozen miles. Hunters probably killed only one animal out of ten. All these factors, together with others such as lean years and epidemics, indicate that under optimal conditions, a thousand square miles of land were required to sustain a group of men during the age of the reindeer. Moreover, such a group tended to split into smaller groups of ten of fifteen individuals in order to facilitate the exploitation of the hunting grounds.

This supposition is based on present-day hunting conditions with respect to the reindeer and does not take into account fishing and the gathering of wild plants or other game animals. Still, it shows that under ideal conditions groups were small. When using direct or indirect evidence, one must assign the imagination to its proper place: its role in any science is to guide, not to supplant, research.

5. THE BIRTH OF THE TOOL

The true primitives were the men before whom the earth belonged only to the animals. Intelligent monkeys were able to pick up sitcks and knock down fruit, but never had they fashioned tools. The first creative act was the work of the most primitive men.

In France these men probably lived in a climate slightly warmer than that of today. Though most of the wild plants were the same as of those of today, the landscapes were different. In the temperate regions there is not one square yard of soil which has not been refashioned by man since the remote age of the first primitives. Only certain uninhabited parts of Argentina or the northern slopes of Tibet give a picture of what the fertile tracts of virgin land were like in France.

An important part of the diet of our remote ancestors consisted, according to the season, of ample supplies of chestnuts, walnuts, acorns, beechnuts, several sprouts, roots and tubers, and edible barks. It is worth noting in passing that most of these foods subsequently diminished in importance as new plants were imported.

The hippopotamus, elephant and rhinoceros were probably too large to be game for the first hunters. But the latter found different kinds of deer, and plenty of horses and boars.

Streams and marshes were filled with fish and turtles. To depict France as a terrestrial paradise for its first inhabitants is to exaggerate the facts. Beasts of prey were numerous, and some winters were like those of modern Italy or the Cote d'Azur. But the quest for food was probably relatively easy.

The only human fossil that can be assigned to the earliest period in the history of man was discovered at Mauer, near Heidelberg, Germany. This is the famous jawbone of the Heidelberg man (see page 37). A jawbone seems like scant evidence for use in reconstructing man, yet it gives a clue to his size, shape of his face, his tongue muscles, and even to some extent his diet.

The creature from Heidelberg was of normal human stature, neither a giant nor a dwarf. He was a primitive Paleanthrope, i.e. higher on the ladder of evolution than the Pithecanthropes but lower than Neanderthal man. The jawbone is huge, chinless, and apparently designed for powerful chewing muscles and weak facial muscles. The teeth, though larger than ours, seem small in relation to the huge jawbone into which they are set. The canines are not tusks. Collectively, they are rather all-purpose teeth—human teeth. Nothing is known of the brain or of the posture of the Heidelberg man. All that is known is that he was a very primitive man with a thick, rather expressionless face. To try to be more specific is to risk giving free reign to the imagination.

Unfortunately, no tool was found near the Heidelberg man's jawbone. The jawbone was found in a sandpit, surrounded by numerous remains of elephants, horses, bears, lions and even saber-toothed tigers. But in strata dating from the same period, excavations in France (chiefly at Abbeville) and England (chiefly at Clacton-on-Sea) have uncovered worked flints. The Heidelberg jawbone and the flints from Abbeville and Clacton make it possible to reconstruct the culture of the most primitive stage of man's history. But first, it is import to distinguish between what is factual and what is simply guesswork:

(1) There is nothing to prove that Heidelberg men fashioned tools since none was found near his jawbone. But he probably did, for the Pithecanthropes and Sinanthropes, who had more primitive jawbones than he, fashioned tools from pebbles; in Algeria traces of the Atlanthrope have been found together with an excellent collection of Clactonian- and Abbevillean-type implements.

(2) The tool-makers of Abbeville and Clacton were probably not similar to the Heidelberg man. Here, nothing either contradicts or denies the statement. But if Heidelberg man worked flints, he was at least capable of making implements similar to those of Abbeville and Clacton. In fact, the processes through which these implements were fashioned are the most primitive imaginable, starting from the time when man first broke a stone to produce a cutting edge.

In short, our first balance-sheet may be summarized as follows: western Europe, at the beginning of the quaternary, when the fauna consisted of animals adapted to a warm climate, was inhabited by men; at least one of these men (the one whose jawbone was discovered) was a primitive Paleanthrope; these men fashioned implements in the primitive style represented by the flints of Abbeville and Clacton. Nothing more is known about these men; much can be learned from their tools.

PRIMITIVE TECHNICS

Let us suppose that we are on the banks of a stream. Swellings have worn away the banks. In an eroded section we see pebbles and blocks of flint. We pick up a rather heavy stone to use as a hammer and select a block of flint weighing four or five pounds. We strike our hammer against the block and make a piece of flint fly off. The sliver is thick and irregular, but its edges are very sharp. We can

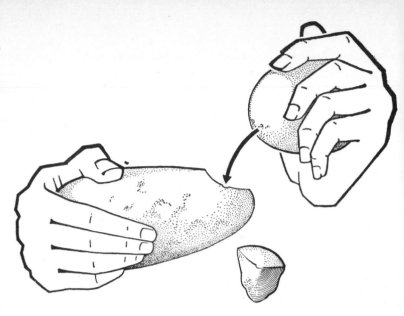

First stage: by striking perpendicularly against the flat edge of a block of stone, primitive man produced a Clactonian sliver which could be used as a knife.

repeat the operation several times on the same stone: each blow will produce a thick, irregular sliver with a *striking surface* and an oblique *cleft surface*. Each blow results in a *Clactonian sliver*, named for Clacton-on-Sea; the simplest product of human ingenuity.

We can imagine creatures who would do no more than to hammer on blocks of flint and produce Clactonian slivers sufficient for cutting up game or fashioning clubs. But the fact is that several successive Clactonian slivers taken from the same block transform what is left of the block—the center or *nucleus*—into a cutting instrument. The most primitive tool-makers thus generally produced two kinds of imple-

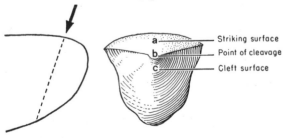

ments: Clactonian slivers and implements fashioned from the nucleus.

TOOLS FASHIONED FROM THE NUCLEUS

Now we select a flat rock weighing about two pounds and strike twice along the edge to produce two Clactonian slivers. The result of this technical operation is a *chopper,* a jagged cutting instrument.

We continue our work by hammering against the smaller end of the stone. With two or three blows, we produce a point: the tool has become a *biface.* It is a thick cutting instrument, keen and long enough to perform the rudimentary tasks assigned to it. It is the characteristic tool of the prehistoric craftsmen of Abbeville.

We have just leafed through the catalog of the most primitive creations of man: the Clactonian sliver, the chopper, the rude biface. These objects have been found, together or separately, in almost all the well-preserved sites of the beginning of the quaternary. To fashion them, primitive man had only to choose rocks or pebbles of the appropriate shape

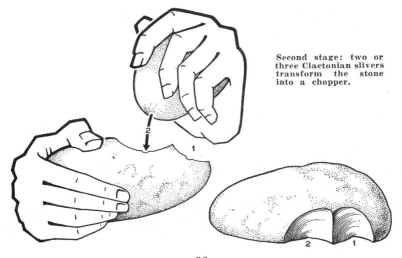

Second stage: two or three Clactonian slivers transform the stone into a chopper.

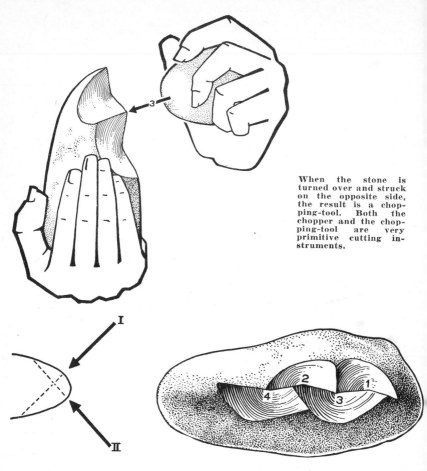

When the stone is turned over and struck on the opposite side, the result is a chopping-tool. Both the chopper and the chopping-tool are very primitive cutting instruments.

and hammer perpendicularly a few times against the striking surfaces. But the process, simple as it was, is far beyond the capacity of a monkey. And in turning the stone over to work the other side, the tool-maker had to use judgment. To choose the surface where he must strike and to produce the point, he had to have a very real sense of the structure of his material and he had to judge the force of his blows; in a word, he had to use foresight.

If modern man should suddenly lose all his accumulated technical knowledge and have to start again from zero, he

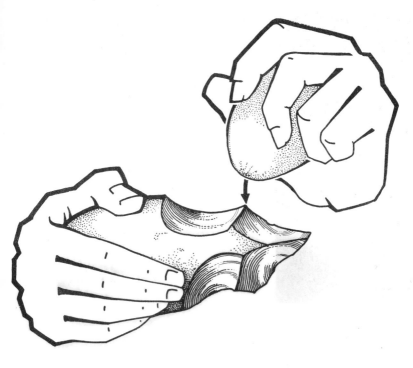

Third stage: A biface—a cutting instrument which, though pointed, is still awkward and heavy—was produced by hammering against the tip of the chopping-tool.

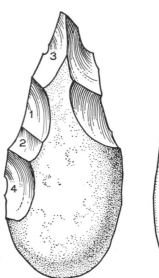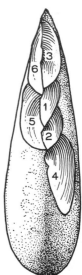

This view of a chopping-tool and a biface (the cutting sides are toward the camera) shows the imprints of the heavy blows that produced their jagged cutting edges.

would probably require several centuries to discover the use of flint. For many generations he would make the only objects that can be fashioned with little training, i.e. Clactonian slivers. He would then succeed in making choppers and, finally, he would discover the admirable cutting properties of the biface.

Among prehistoric men, the same pattern was followed. From the Clactonian sliver to the chopper, from the chopper to the first rude biface, there was *progress*. Progress was possible because the initial series of achievements was preserved from one generation to the next. This was the earliest *technical tradition*. From the time the tradition was established, the size of the brain decreased in importance. Men who were sufficiently human to fashion tools were already capable of transmitting their technical tradition unchanged until the day when some ingenious successor, of the same or a different race, added to their achievements or contributed his own, which would in turn become a part of the common tradition.

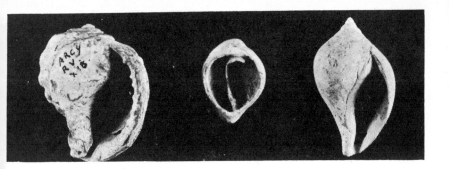

Sea shells were fancied during the later part of the Paleolithic period and caves near the banks of streams contain great quantities of pierced shells used as earrings, necklaces and ornaments for the hair. Strangely enough, at Arcy, hundreds of miles from the sea, are found the same shells, pierced and sawed, which the men of the age of the reindeer procured, not directly but by digging into the sands deposited during the tertiary period when the sea, long before, had covered the region around Paris.   (Plate by Musée de l'Homme.)

6. THE FIRST ARTISTS

The period of Abbevillean and Clactonian craftsmanship was followed by a severe glacial period, perhaps the Mindel. The hippopotamus and other animals too sensitive to the cold disappeared forever from the regions of France.

What happened during this time to the men of the preceding period? No one knows. Surprisingly enough, no document dating from the Mindel glaciation has been found. Still, when we compare traces of the pre-glacial and post-glacial periods, we note (and this is less surprising) that they are in complete harmony, as if there had never been a rupture in either their craftsmanship or their racial characteristics. The post-glacial tools follow exactly the Abbevillean and Clactonian tradition, and skeletal remains of Paleanthropes indicate a close relation to Heidelberg man.

Our knowledge of the events that took place during the Riss glaciation is also limited. It is worth noting that geologists are not in complete agreement concerning the number, duration and temperature of the glacial periods. Available documents dating from the intervals of warmer climate that separated the Mindel and Riss glaciations and, later, the Riss and Würm glaciations suggest that human life continued during the glacial periods.

The climate during the warmer intervals hardly differed from our own. There were colder periods, but they came thousands of years apart (except, of course, during the Riss glaciation when the temperature dropped sharply). The landscape was almost the same as that described in chapter 5: oak, beech, walnut and box-wood in forested and limestone regions, wild vines on the sunny slopes. The fauna still included a few species that are now extinct, such as the elephant and the Merck rhinoceros, but was by and large the same as today: the red deer, roe deer, hart, castor, horse and wild ox.

In this secluded part of one of the caves at Arcy, the floor on which the Mousterians lived was left intact. In the middle of a pile of stones lie the broken bones of horses and reindeer and the flint tools abandoned tens of thousands of years ago by Paleanthrope hunters.   (Plate by P. Poulain.)

THREE TYPES OF MEN

The period discussed in this chapter is the longest in the history of humanity. It probably lasted several hundred thousand years. The human relics that date from it are divided into two geographical groups:

(1) *The western group.*—A cranial cap from Swanscombe (England). A cranial cap from Fontechevade (France).

(2) *The eastern group.*—A jawless cranium from Steinheim (Germany). A cranium and part of a skeleton from Ehringsdorf (Germany).

(3) *The southern and central group.*—A jawless cranium from Gibraltar. Two craniums, also without jaws, from Saccopastore (Italy). An upper jaw and a lower jaw from Arcy (France).

An interesting fact (but one that might be contradicted by new discoveries) is that each geographical group corresponds to a rather definite racial type.

The western group consists of cranial caps which are almost like those of modern men. The shape of their faces is not known, but was probably more like ours than like the others. Their relics have been found in the places where prehistoric cultures reached their highest point.

The eastern group is also very striking. The relics from Ehringsdorf indicate that these Paleanthropes had prominent eyebrows and receding chins; in contrast, their foreheads were developed like those of modern races. The Steinheim cranium resembles those of the western group but has huge eyebrows. In short, the human relics of the western group belonged to very different epochs and races but have some modern characteristics.

The southern and central group is the most primitive. The brain is small, the skull very flat, the eyebrows prominent. But the Arcy jaw (the one named Augustine by my students) has a true chin and several advanced characteristics.

Floors as well preserved as the one shown on page 58 are rarely found; the relics are usually covered by mud and piled in several layers. This section of an Arcy cave shows strata 16 through 20 (the floor seen on page 58 corresponds to stratum 16, not shown here). Stratum 20, shown in the foreground, is the same as the floor on which Augustine lived. The bones were dug out of clay and the droppings of hyenas. They indicate that the Paleanthropes ate especially the horse, aurochs and reindeer, and sometimes the red deer or roe deer. Also shown are the bones of wolves and hyenas. This photograph was taken a short time before the discovery of Augustine, found a yard farther north. Another human jaw was discovered two days later only four inches behind the lower tip of the vertical ruler. (Plate by Leroi-Gourhan.)

THE PALEANTHROPES OF ARCY-SUR-CURE

Most of the human relics of the interglaciary period have been discovered in quarries, buried in the sand. Thus we know little of their way of life. The only ones about whom we have much information are the ancient inhabitants of the Arcy-Sur-Cure cave. The floor on which they lived was covered by eight more recent strata, and each stratum had to be worked through inch by inch to guard against losing the slightest clue.

We have recovered, by tiny bits (sometimes but one tooth), the relics of six or seven individuals: at least two adults and several children or adolescents. Their cave was dark and damp. A path leading to passage-ways hundreds of yards long crossed the cave. During the times when the cave was not occupied by men, bears came there to sleep and sometimes to die. Hyenas prowled through the passageways devouring the dead bodies of bears and men; their droppings, which fossilize perfectly since they are rich in calcium, were found in the cave; along the path these droppings formed a layer some eight inches thick, and throughout the rest of the cave they formed a solid mat. In summer, Augustine and her family must have preferred an outdoor camp, but in winter they had to return to their cave and live among the droppings and carcasses, including the remains of old hyenas which had ended their existence at the scene of their feasts. They settled down in the middle of the cave, simply brushing aside the most bulky bones. No preserved fireplace has been found, but here and there appear burned stones and tiny bits of burned bone.

The Paleanthropes must have eaten many vegetable sprouts, roots and fruits. Their teeth (like those of their peers in Italy) bear the marks of intense trituration. But they were also hunters of oxen and horses, and skilled butchers. They dismembered slain animals on the spot and dragged large portions inside the cave. They apparently cut off the legs and heads of oxen and horses, discarding the rest of the carcass. Everything carried away was consumed; the bones were scraped clean, then broken in order that the marrow could be extracted. The remains were carelessly cast behind, against the walls. In this way there was formed around this central lair a thick girdle of the left-overs from horses and oxen as well as from the first reindeer and mammoths brought back to France by the approach of the Würm glaciation. Occasionally among this household garbage are found human relics, also broken into small bits. To what extent does their presence indicate cannabilism? It is difficult to answer this question, but cannabilism would be, after all, an indication of humanity, for men are the only primates that readily devour each other!

During the bad seasons plant foods became scarce and meat, too, was probably hard to get. It is easy to visualize these men then, with their low foreheads and jutting snouts, burrowed in their sleeping quarters, squatting among the filth of the hyenas, scratching and gnawing on the carcasses of horses. Perhaps the teeth of one of them were worn off even with the gums as a result of the action of his formidable jaws, and masses of abscesses had worked deep into the bone.

The inhabitants of Arcy seem to have been real savages, even considering the time during which they lived. The way in which they worked flint, though they applied correct techniques, was coarse. The western and eastern Palean-thropes, with their larger craniums, were doubtless more advanced. But their patterns of living were probably not marked by excessive gentility. The Fontechevade man was apparently killed by a fell blow on the top of his cranium, while the Steinheim man was the victim of some disaster that cost him a fourth of his face; both are suspiciously mixed in with culinary debris.

THE ACHEULEAN ARTS AND CRAFTS

The preceding chapter stopped at the moment when the tool-maker had learned to strike a block of flint perpendicularly and remove Clactonian slivers, creating rude choppers and bifaces. These tools were heavy and their cutting edge was crooked. From the outset of the new period, craftsmen fall into three groups:

(1) Those who used the old method of perpendicular blows with little modification of the former creations (such as the Fontechevade man).

(2) Those who perfected the art in the regions where large blocks of good-quality flint were plentiful.

(3) Those who were reduced to expending their creative imagination on a scant supply of small, low-quality rocks.

Thus progress depended on complex factors. It varied according to the skills of the workmen, which differed from one race to the next, and according to the disparate quality of available raw materials, ranging from big blocks of flint weighing several pounds to tiny opaque lumps difficult to fracture.

The *Acheulean* products of the Somme and the lower Seine resulted from the union of a high level of workmanship and an abundance of suitable raw materials. The name derives from Saint-Acheul, on the Somme (France), where many worked flints were found, and is applied to the civilization which these implements represent.

The Acheulean style of workmanship is distinct. A flat, oval piece of flint was selected. Then the workman directed a clean, glancing blow against the edge of the stone (instead of hammering away, as before, against its flat side). The result was a longer and flatter sliver than the Clactonian. The blows were directed alternately to the right and to the left, up and down the rounded side of the stone. The result was a flat biface with an uneven rim. A few deft blows removed the irregularities, and the final product was a good flint nucleus with a rectilinear cutting edge and a shape that was both balanced and efficient.

The block of flint might first be trimmed in the Clactonian style, then chipped along the sides with the same hammer. To finish his implement, the workman might strike it lengthwise with a hard stick. This was the high point in Acheulean workmanship: the magnificent flint "dabs" found in the regions where beautiful rocks were plentiful.

From the viewpoint of progress, the craftsmanship of this period has considerable significance. Not just a single family of accomplishments, but several successive series form a very complex chain:

(1) Choosing an appropriate piece of flint in which the mind had foreseen the form of the implement to be fashioned;

(2) Trimming it by using the minimum number of Clactonian devices;

(3) Working lengthwise (a new accomplishment) to give the piece of flint its pre-final shape;

(4) Using a wooden hammering device (a new accomplishment and a new implement) for flat, precision trimming lengthwise.

Such a chain evinces real human intelligence even if thousands of years were required for its development and successive workmen were conscious of almost no change.

The forces that inspired the evolution are obvious. The first is technical: the new cutting edge was superior to the old, and the magnificent Acheulean dab was a most efficient implement. The second is economical: from two pounds of flint the man from Clacton or Abbeville fashioned a rude biface with a jagged cutting edge scarcely two inches long; from the same quantity of flint the Acheulean workman fashioned two dabs, each with a good cutting edge more than six inches long. But flint quarries were not found everywhere, and cutting implements wear out very quickly: thus the mobility of the Acheulean hunter was four times greater

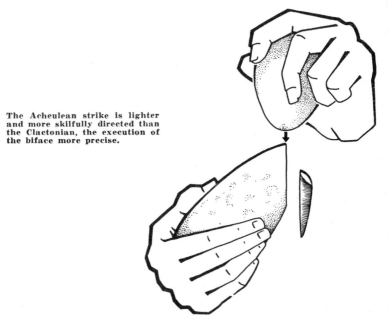

The Acheulean strike is lighter and more skilfully directed than the Clactonian, the execution of the biface more precise.

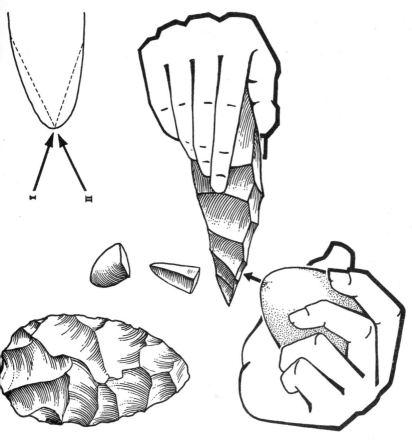

than that of his predecessors. From the very beginning the problems of economic geography were very important; the evolution of man in its entirety was motivated mainly by his dependence on sources of raw materials.

TRIANGULAR POINTS AND LEVALLOISAN SLIVERS

The biface, despite the progress made, remained heavy and cumbersome. It had the qualities and the shortcomings of an all-purpose implement: it could be used to cut, to puncture, to scrape and to dig when necessary, but all this without precision. Moreover, the biface was rather hard to

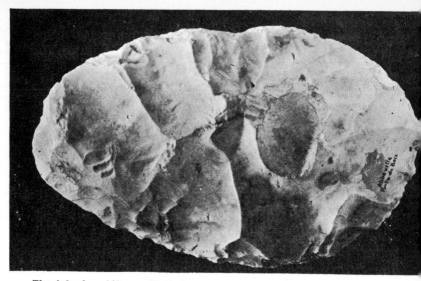

The Acheulean biface, with its long grooves and evenly trimmed sides, had a regular shape and was more efficient than the Abbevillean biface.
(Plate by G. Tendron.)

fashion; the process required time. Before it had even reached its apogee, better implements had been found.

The workman could, by removing Clactonian slivers from a block of stone weighing several pounds, trim off the rough exterior and prepare good striking surfaces. By combining Clactonian and lengthwise strikes, he could rim the stone with large facets. The block was ready for the fabrication of a new instrument. On the upper side small grooves above the ridge formed by adjacent facets provided a good striking surface. A light tap near the rim freed a small sliver. A second, aimed a little farther back from the rim and heavier than the first, freed an admirably shaped *triangular point,* varying from three to five inches in length. The point was reinforced at the tip by its sides, its cutting edges were sharper than the biface, and its base, thin and flat, could be fitted into a handle or staff to serve as a blade or pike.

Besides, the yield was considerable. From a pound of raw materials the worker fashioned, on the average, four flints—

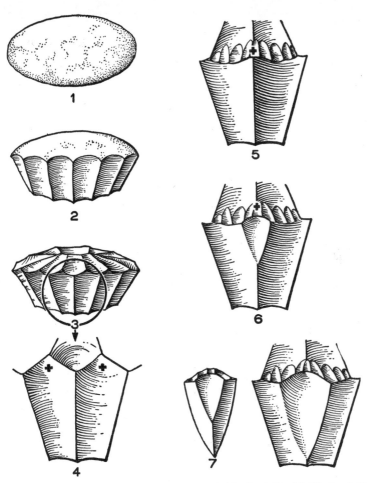

Stages in the fabrication of the triangular point in "serial": (1) Block of raw flint. (2) The shell is chipped away to give a series of evenly-spaced facets. (3) The top is dressed to provide a good striking surface. (4) A grooved striking surface directly over a convex ridge. (5) The finishing touches in the preparation of a good striking surface. (6) The initial thinning operation. (7) The final strike which produces the finished product.

about a yard of cutting surface. A supply of from ten to fifteen pounds of points would last for several months and allow the hunter to leave his home and travel some sixty miles to search out the Merck rhinoceros in the best feeding grounds.

But that is not all. The nucleus still remained. As one sliver after another was removed, it acquired the shape and size of a terrapin's carapace. The workman trimmed the better end to produce a good striking surface. Then with a final stroke (very difficult to administer properly), he sheered off a magnificent sheet of flint, flat and as long as his hand, with thin, sharp edges: a *Levalloisan sliver*. This he kept in the fold of his bearskin covering. Its uses were many: in its present condition it was good for carving; slight modifications would result in a very fine biface.

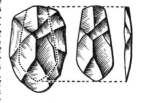

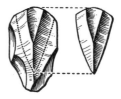

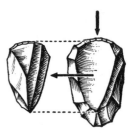

The Levalloisan nucleus. Comparison of this diagram with the one on the preceding page shows that the blocks are prepared in the same way except that instead of chipping away at the wider circumference of the stone, the worker here takes the slivers from the large, flat end. Special preparation of the surface makes it possible for the worker to extract at will a triangular point, a wide sliver or a blade.

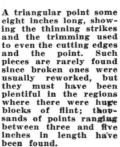

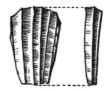

A triangular point some eight inches long, showing the thinning strikes and the trimming used to even the cutting edges and the point. Such pieces are rarely found since broken ones were usually reworked, but they must have been plentiful in the regions where there were huge blocks of flint; thousands of points ranging between three and five inches in length have been found.

But these implements were produced in a region where big blocks of flint were plentiful. In other regions, where game was plentiful, flint existed only in the form of small lumps scarcely twice the size of a fist. Here mass production was a challenge. The workman took up an unpromising lump of flint and transformed it into a "terrapin's carapace" (a rather small one, to be sure). Then he prepared the flatter surface, either by chipping all around the rim or by making one or several parallel ridges, and effected a Levalloisan sliver. The chipped surface resulted in a normal Levalloisan sliver. A single facet gave a very satisfactory triangular point (but only one for each nucleus). Several facets . . . but that comes a few thousand years later and is the subject matter of the next chapter.

Thus a veritable technical revolution took place during this stage, called Moustero-Levalloisan (from the caves at Moustier, Dordogne, and Levallois-Perret, near Paris). Man made free use of all the possibilities acquired during preceding periods. The flint specialists used in turn the Clactonian style of cutting, the style used in the fabrication of the biface and the lateral method of cutting, with the same degree of craftsmanship and technical mastery as the modern joiner who selects his wood, studies its good qualities and shortcomings, applies blows and stresses, anticipates, corrects, and coordinates all his actions.

These skills were acquired before the beginning of the Würm glaciation, at a time when the physical structure of the men, as revealed by skeletal remains, was still rather disconcerting. In spite of his repulsive appearance and all that we know of his coarse life, the Arcy man, who was probably a somber savage lost at the foot of the mountain, was not completely lacking in skill. He knew how to fashion points in the carapace style from the low-quality lumps of flint found in his region. As for the men of the western group, they had points more than six inches long, retouched and shaped not merely with skill but with artistry.

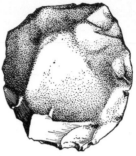

These two pieces were found near the remains of Augustine,
halfway between the jaw and the bones shown on page 60.
Both are from a nucleus shaped like a terrapin's carapace.
A wide sliver was removed from one, a Levalloisan sliver
from the other. Even from such unsuitable materials as the available supply
of lumps of flint, the Arcy man managed to fashion tools in the most modern
style (for his epoch).

In fact, on examining the most beautiful of the worked
flints of this period, one senses that here art began its evolution. We have no plastic works from the period; if such ever
existed, they have disappeared. But here we find functional
esthetics, i.e. the search in the fabrication of implements for
the most beautiful and efficient forms, as in aerodynamics.

7. THE LAST PRIMITIVES

Man had traveled far by the time the Würm glaciation began. Though from forty to eighty thousand years were to elapse before recorded history began, three-fourths of the span of man's existence had been completed. We have a much clearer picture of this period than of the preceding. Before the Würm glaciation, water repeatedly invaded the caverns, with the result that we can count on the fingers of one hand those which have preserved strata antedating the glaciation. After the glaciation, however, the caves are filled with vestiges which have been preserved until today.

During the first part of the glaciation, France was inhabited by strange creatures belonging to the Neanderthal race. More advanced men existed, but they probably lived farther to the south, perhaps in Asia Minor. The climate of these regions was then temperate and areas which are barren today were covered with vegetation. Relics of Paleanthropes closely resembling the Neanthropes have been uncovered in Palestine. But the western regions, with their cold, damp climate, were probably abandoned by the superior men of the epoch. The men whose relics have been found in France apparently belonged to a backward race. For several milleniums the Neanderthalians—the last of the low-browed Paleanthropes—roamed over the hunting grounds of France.

At Arcy-sur-Cure we uncovered nine strata dating from this period. Thus we have a general notion of the changes that occurred. The Würm glaciation was not a uniformly cold period. Several different times the temperature rose only to drop again.

Stage 1.—The climate was mild. The landscape was the same as that of modern France (without cultivation, of course). Many horses and wild cattle. A few red deer and wild boars. Augustine and her family moved into the cave and led the existence described earlier.

Stage 2.—Intense cold, which was to subside gradually during the stages marked by the next two strata, set in. Many reindeer, a few horses, some chamois that had sought refuge in the lower regions, and polar foxes. Mousterian civilization slowly developed.

Stage 3.—The cold was less severe. Some reindeer still, several horses and a few wild boars. The climate was fairly dry.

Stage 4.—Rain. Thawing and trickling streams. Through the fissures of the cave came streams of mud that settled in a thick blanket over the previous strata. Man was elsewhere, in drier regions.

Stage 5.—The forest returned. The weather was good. Reindeer were scarce. Herds of horses and cattle were the common game. Small wild asses came back from the southern part of France with the big red deer and wild boars. The civilization of the Neanderthalians had changed; that the men worked with wood is indicated by their discarded flint planes; they kept the Mousterian stock of implements but added several tools later found in the hands of *Homo sapiens,* like carinated planes and gravers, and they hunted with round stones and slingshots. Better still, they collected curiosities, and this is the first step in the direction of art. That was the final flash of the Paleanthropian civilization; doubtless the last Paleanthropes were influenced by the art and skills of groups of *Homo sapiens,* who were not too far away.

Stage 6.—Confusion. Was it the effect of climatic changes and the thaw? Or did the volcanoes of Auvergne suddenly erupt? The ceilings of the caves gave way, tightly sealing the old strata. This was the knell of the great Mousterian civilization.

Stage 7.—The last primitives returned to the debris of the caves to seek shelter from the elements. They were apparently exiles, their craftsmanship wretched. They collected and reworked their ancestors' flints and fashioned their implements on rude rocks wherever they chanced to lie. The cold returned.

Stage 8.—Extremely cold. Reindeer and polar foxes reappeared. But a new civilization was arising: that of the age of the reindeer, which will again appear in the next chapter.

At Arcy, no human relics were found in strata 3, 4, 5 or 6, but in about fifty other caves of France and western Europe, skeletal remains of Neanderthalians have been found in corresponding strata. The Arcy cave did, however, contain a few faint human traces in strata 7 and 8; these are the men who witnessed the crumbling of the ceilings and a complete change in their civilization. Strangely enough, these men were still Paleanthropes, but we are not well enough acquainted with them to know whether or not they were exactly like the Neanderthalians.

THE LIFE OF NEANDERTHAL MAN

France was peopled by Neanderthalians during a long period that embraces strata 2, 3, 4 and 5. The climate was damp and rather cold during most of the period but milder toward the end. The population was probably relatively dense, to judge from the hundreds of thousands of discarded flint implements found in almost every region. To be sure, there are fewer zones containing skeletal remains, but that is

73

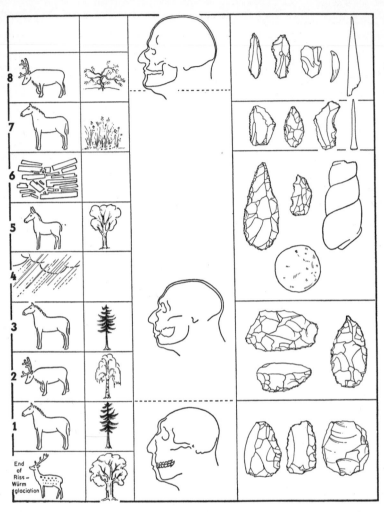

Climatic table of the Mousterian Culture

because human relics resisted the elements only in the limestone regions where there were caves.

Wherever fossil humans dating from this period are found, they represent Neanderthalians, and their implements are Mousterian. Still, there are variations from one region to the next and probably from one period to the next; the successive strata of Arcy give a striking picture of the continuous evolution of the Mousterian civilization.

The Neanderthal men were still Paleanthropes, i.e. creatures that one would almost hesitate to consider true humans, so repugnant was their physical appearance. We have seen, however, that they were human in their technical capacity. Besides, long before them, flint-workers had handed down the fine points of their craft and they, with their blocks of flint in their hands, thought in exactly the same way as a modern man who creates something. The important question at this point concerns the religious and artistic activities of Neanderthal man. The smallest indication of either activity would draw him much closer to us. According to our own personal convictions, we may conclude either that the primitives were led progressively to formulate beliefs to protect them from the fear of death or that they shared in divine revelation. In either case, such preoccupations would bind them more closely to modern man.

Available information about the religious and artistic life of the Neanderthalians, though scant, is definite. The skeletal remains from La Chappelle-aux-Saintes were found lying in a sepulcher. The adolescent whose remains were found at Moustier had also been buried, and at La Ferrassie excavations have uncovered several hand-made sepulchers containing especially well-wrought flint offerings. At Arcy, poor Augustine, far from having been interred by her contemporaries, had probably paid the cost of a farewell banquet; but this act of cannibalism belonged to an earlier period. At Arcy, in the stratum corresponding to the relatively mild period that preceded the age of the reindeer, we found a grave containing the relics of a human body, unfortunately almost completely decomposed.

In short the Neanderthalians (at least those who lived before the age of the reindeer) buried their dead; sometimes they even had some sort of burial ceremony. Besides, in the course of their wanderings they collected unusual stones and

One of the oldest known amateur collections: a piece of fool's gold, a fossil shell of the secondary period, and a polypier from the same period. All were found in the last strata of the Mousterian period among flint implements and the bones of animals. The curiosities were found far away from the caves where the Paleanthropes lived and carried by them to their habitat.
(Plate by Musée de l'Homme.)

fossil shells. Certainly from their age must date the beginnings of the most noble activities of human thought.

Another fascinating problem is that of the development of speech. When did men first begin to communicate with each other by speaking?

Certainly speech already existed, at least in a rudimentary form, among the Anthropes responsible for the Clacto-Abbevillean culture. That is all the more reason why their Neanderthal successors, with their more complicated works and their concern over the dead, must have had a richer language to express more accurately their thoughts. Their brains were as large as ours; though organized somewhat differently, they also, perhaps, included the faculty of speech. In any event, the shape of the face and signs of tongue muscles give the impression that mimicry and speech movements were not so easy for them as for us.

It is easy to believe that in their social life the Neanderthalians had the basic unit, the family. But beyond that, how were they organized? Did they live in bands or in tribes? Did they single out family groups and chieftains? The answers to these questions are not inscribed in the

One of the last Alakaluf Indians of Tierra del Fuego. His grandparents still led an existence comparable to that of the last Neanderthalians. If his forehead were lower and his eyebrow ridges more pronounced, his face would not differ much from that suggested by the skulls of Neanderthalians.
(Plate by Emperaire.)

book of the earth. We can only apply to the Neanderthalians the rule applied to all peoples who live by hunting: the size of the group is proportional to the supply of game on the accessible territory. In practice, this means that Neanderthal groups rarely numbered more than a few individuals, though several groups might on occasion band together to hunt migratory game.

No existing tribe on the face of the earth is comparable to the Neanderthalians. But the indigenous Australians and the Indians of Tierra del Fuego still offered a fairly good picture, half a century ago, of the life of the Neanderthalians. This is especially true of the inhabitants of Tierra del Fuego, where the climate, at the southern tip of the American continent, is quite similar to the cold, damp climate which must have characterized Europe at the beginning of the Würm glaciation.

Only a few years ago the Fuegians still lived in small groups comprising a few families, just large enough to get sufficient food without exceeding the resources of their hunting grounds. Fish and game were the staples of their diet, but they had to fall back on other foods to survive during times of scarcity—just any edible product that could be obtained from wild plants and small animals, even including

77

insects. They lived in hemispherical huts made of brush and boughs. There they crowded around a fire fed insofar as possible with bits of broken bones. They had a strong resistance to cold: as his only garment, the Fuegian wore a square pelt, draped over his shoulder like a bandóleer, just big enough to cover his body when he squatted down with his back to the wind. Their domestic equipment was reduced to the minimum: baskets woven in the simplest style, bone-pointed harpoons, pebbles that served as hammers or grinders, and flint planes and knives. The modern world offers no better example of what the life of the Neanderthalians must have been like.

To picture the implements of the Neanderthalians, it is not necessary to seek out other tribes. Prehistoric sites have provided enough samples to give an exact portrait.

The last chapter stopped with the technical Moustero-

In some ways this group of Australians suggests what might have been a Paleanthropian encampment. The hut formed from boughs, the wooden weapons, some baskets which Neanderthalians probably knew how to construct, and a few flint tools—all these, together with the naked men seated on a littered floor around the hearth, give an unflattering picture of a Mousterian encampment.   (Plate by Musée de l'Homme.)

Levalloisan revolution. Since they had learned to work with small chunks of flint, the hunters were no longer constrained to remain in the immediate proximity of quarries. They had only to make an occasional trip and bring back a few pounds of raw materials, then transform them into all-purpose implements—triangular points and scrapers.

This is precisely the stage that the cave-dwellers of Arcy had reached at the time represented by the first stage of the climatic table (see page 74). Augustine's husband worked his small chunks of flint economically and obtained from them triangular points and scrapers. He could also find other uses for smaller slivers and remnants from the nucleus.

His successors again took up the tradition, and during stages 2 and 3 of the climatic table (very cold and moderately so), they continued to cut up flint with a yield of about two yards of cutting surface per pound. But they were probably more industrious or better informed: instead of gathering the pebbles from Cure and the meager lumps of flint from the cliff, they traveled some twenty miles to find good flint in the caves. This had a favorable effect on production. Their tools were also more varied: alongside their points and scrapers are found planes and notched pieces, indicating that the shafts of their weapons were carefully fashioned. Direct evidence of boar-spears and lances has disappeared, for these weapons were made of wood.

Then came the rainy period of stage 4. The warmer temperature brought back to France red deer and wild boars.

The two most popular implements among the Mousterians: the triangular point, which might have been used as a spearhead or knife; and the scraper, which was probably used to scrape pelts but which seems also to have been favored as a knife for dressing game, cutting meat, and performing a thousand other household tasks.

(Plate by G. Tendron.)

This display summarizes the tens of thousands of years that separate the Mousterian period from the age of the reindeer. The implements are arranged chronologically according to the place where they were found in the soil.

To the right are Mousterian slivers: the scraper and the triangular point. To the left are upper paleolithic laminated tools: the graver and the jagged-edged blade.

Stratum 17 corresponds to the apogee of the Mousterian period.

Strata 14 and 10 represent the passage from the chipping to the laminated style. A real transition is observable: the graver and jagged-edged blade in 14 are chipped as are the old Perigordian point and scraper in 10. Stratum 7 is middle Perigordian.

Apparently it also caused different men to move northward. In any event, Augustine's descendants came into contact with a new civilization, no longer the Mousterian civilization but still not that of the age of the reindeer. This marks a dark, intermediate period. Doubtless it became difficult to reach the quarries across the great forest, for the men economized in their use of raw materials, working the smallest fragments and reworking old implements, the finished product sometimes being no larger than a fingernail. The good flint was saved for the points of weapons; pebbles and small chunks of flint were made into scrapers, planes and the first gravers.

The style was still Moustero-Levalloisan. The implements were heavy and thick, and did not measurably surpass a yield of a yard of cutting surface per pound. But progress is apparent: the types of implements were more varied. They included points, scrapers, planes, big scratching-knives, gravers and the first backed knives. All these implements indicate that wood-working had become progressively more important.

In addition to chipped-flint implements, they frequently hammered out balls of sandstone and limestone. The hunters probably tied them to thongs in pairs and used them to strike and entangle game, in much the same way as the people of southern Argentina, near the Fuegians, use *boleadores*.

The age of the reindeer was not far away. The last actor was ready to make his appearance on the stage of prehistory. He was our equal, *Homo sapiens* ("wise-man" as he chose to designate himself), with a wide forehead and a versatile brush which he used to adorn the walls of caves.

With its wooded slopes, this Tibetan landscape suggests certain regions of France during the age of the reindeer. The plant life of the valley, leveled by the action of frost and snow, shows that the region lies in a latitude where the sun is warm in the summertime. (Plate by Guibaut-Liotard.)

8. THE AGE OF THE REINDEER

Homo sapiens appeared in Europe during the second half of the Würm glaciation. There our equal was to develop the civilization of the age of the reindeer. Some specialists fix the date of this event at approximately forty thousand years before our era, others at only twenty thousand. Since the Würm glaciation was the last one, it is possible to study the steady retreat of the old glaciers by observing the strata of silt deposited year by year as they moved northward. Calculations based on silt deposits in Scandinavian and Canadian lakes indicate that the Würm glaciation—and the age of the reindeer—ended some eight or ten thousand years before our era began.

This is the first definite date in the whole history of man. It means that the age of the reindeer lasted at least ten thousand years and that ten thousand more years elapsed between the age of the reindeer and the present.

After the damp, cold period that Neanderthal man had experienced, the climate became somewhat milder; in the second half of the Würm glaciation, it became very cold and dry. The game of the earlier period returned—horses and wild cattle; but this time the reindeer clearly predominated. There were also bisons, mammoths, woolly rhinoceros, wild goats and, in northwestern France, the odd sheeplike antelope of the cold steppes of Europe and central Asia, the saiga. Carnivores were plentiful, especially the wolf, which usually accompanied and took an interest in the herds of reindeer.

The landscape resembled that of present-day Siberia. Its arctic appearance was due to the presence of massive glaciers which covered the Alps and the Pyrenees. Lichen-covered tundra alternated with marshlands dotted with small pines and willows. Continental winds extended the steppe far beyond the glacial regions; forests grew in protected areas along the streams. Such an environment favored the multiplication of large game, and variable streams fed by melting glaciers were conducive to the development of salmon and trout—with the result that the climate of the last half of the Würm glaciation, far from repelling man, must have offered bountiful supplies of game and fish.

In France the only human traces antedating the Würm glaciation are those of the Paleanthropes, especially the Neanderthalians. This does not mean that in other parts of the world there were no men like us at the time when the Paleanthropes still peopled western Europe, but rather that the damp cold and the thick forest barred outsiders. In fact, luxuriant forests are not the favorite habitat of the hunter, for there the game is usually sparse. After the climate had become warmer for a short period of time, the temperature probably dropped again and the climate became dry and cold. The Paleanthropes who still lived in France probably witnessed the arrival of great herds of reindeer together with the hunters of a more advanced race who followed them.

The exact nature of the first contacts between the old race and the new is not known. One thing is certain: from that moment on, there is no trace of Neanderthal man.

HOMO SAPIENS

The newcomers, though distinct from the Paleanthropes, were not all alike.

From the outset of the age of the reindeer there lived in France men similar to the one whose cranium was discovered in the Cro-Magnon cave at Les Eyzies. They were very tall (about six feet and three inches), and had elongated craniums and short faces. Two or three other specimens of the "Cro-Magnon race" were discovered at Dordogne and near Monaco.

For the same period, discoveries include about ten creatures rather closely related to the Cro-Magnon man, but still different. Some are large, others average; some have slightly shorter craniums, others slightly shorter faces. Obviously Cro-Magnon men did not live everywhere, and in different regions there was as much racial variation as today.

For the same period, two rather curious human types are

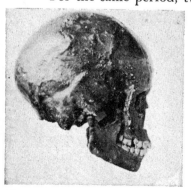

The skull of the young "Negroid" Grimaldi. This is one of the mysteries of prehistoric anthropology, for at first sight this skull resembles that of a young African. But his youth and the shape of each cranial region suggests rather a close kinship to the type of Cro-Magnon who had not yet acquired the appearance of an adult, whose teeth were large with respect to the size of his jaws, and who had also been flattened a little through burial. Quite apart from that, there is nothing to prove that he had black skin and kinky hair. (Plate by Musée de l'Homme.)

worth noting. At Grimaldi, near Monaco, an adolescent was found in a grave that also contained the relics of an aged woman. The woman is of no particular interest, but the young man has occasioned heated discussions among specialists. His appearance suggests that of a young Negro; he has an elongated cranium, a smooth, straight forehead, and projecting incisors. Some specialists conclude that Negroes lived along the Cote d'Azur; others think that the present form of his cranium is probably due to flattening by the weight of the earth.

The other remarkable skeleton, found at Combe-Capelle, in Dordogne, is that of an average-sized man with both an elongated cranium and a long face.

In short, about a hundred human relics dating from the age of the reindeer have been found. Aside from the beclouded case of the Grimaldi adolescent, they all have characteristics of the white race. But the oldest *Homo sapiens* found in Asia or in Africa belonged to the great races who live on those continents today. Thus the division into Whites, Yellows and Blacks was the same in prehistoric times as now.

To summarize: during the whole duration of the age of the reindeer, Europe—and especially France—was peopled by men who differed slightly among themselves and who also differed slightly from modern man; but these men were so like us that it is entirely correct to state that with them present-day mankind began.

LAMINATED FLINT

Students of prehistory single out several currents in the civilization of the age of the reindeer. The names of these currents recall the locations of prehistoric sites:

The *Perigordian* (because of numerous prehistoric caves of Perigord) and the *Aurignacian* (from Aurignac) mark the beginning of the age of the reindeer.

The *Solutrean* (from Solutre) comes next, at least in some regions.

The *Magdalenian* (from the Madeleine cave in Dordogne) ends the age of the reindeer.

All have common characteristics as well as the special traits which led to their being classed separately.

Chapter 6 stopped

FROM A POUND

OF FLINT

THE ABBEVILLEAN OBTAINED
2 INCHES OF CUTTING SURFACE

2 INCHES

THE ACHEULEAN OBTAINED

8 INCHES

THE MOUSTERIAN OBTAINED

40 INCHES

THE MAGDALENIAN OBTAINED

FROM 10 TO 40 FEET

with the longitudinal chipping of a nucleus of flint. Laminated flint carries the process one step farther. The workman struck the nucleus in such a way as to free long, narrow slivers without points but rather with parallel edges. These slivers were *blades,* and from the day the hunters learned to produce them, his pattern of existence was profoundly changed.

From a pound of raw material, the Mousterian flintworkers obtained forty inches of cutting surface, a respectable yield which allowed them to spend months away from the flint quarries. With the chipping of flint into blades, the men of the age of the reindeer increased the yield still more: ten to fifteen feet per pound for coarse blades, thirty to forty feet per pound for fine blades and lamellae. To that must be added the waste, the preparatory slivers, and the blades broken during their use, all of which still served, depending on their shape, as special tools. Freedom with respect to sources of flint was almost completely achieved: whether directly or by barter, hunters could procure the minimum quantity of raw material for fashioning their weapons and tools.

A backward glance will bring out the importance of this technical revolution. The Acheulean craftsmen were riveted to the regions where flint or a good substitute was available. The map showing the places where Acheulean objects have been found is almost empty for the regions with no stone suitable for the fabrication of instruments. During the Moustero-Levalloisan stage, man extended his range; on the map, flint implements exceed the regions where the raw material was found, but large blank areas are numerous and often, in regions distant from flint quarries, only the most important weapons were fashioned from the precious material, the others being shaped insofar as possible from inferior rocks. For the age of the reindeer, the blank spaces on the map are filled: henceforth man roamed everywhere, discarding worn-out implements fashioned from good flint.

Does this point to the conclusion that the chipping of flint into blades was discovered by *Homo sapiens?* Lamination is no more than a further development of older skills, and it is possible that the first worker who practiced it was still a Paleanthrope. But it was surely *Homo sapiens* who caused lamination to spread. Wherever blades are found, men similar to us once lived. The characteristic trait of the craftsmanship of the age of the reindeer is the general use of flint blades as the point of departure of a great number of implements. The blades were reworked, shaped for use as knives, scrapers, punches or gravers.

Each stage developed its own types of implements (see

87

The graver and the scraper are the implements common to all the upper Paleolithic period. They are worked implements of bone, ivory, and reindeer antlers. Near the ends of the graver are the marks left by the removal of lamellae — small, sharp, and very tough (that flint scratches steel is common knowledge). The shapes of gravers vary, this one being of the popular "angular" type. The tips of the scraper were reworked to produce rounded cutting edges like those of some carpenter's planes. (Plate by G. Tendron.)

page 93). But two are common the reindeer: gravers and scrapers.

The graver appeared long before the age of the reindeer, at the beginning of the Acheulean stage, but only occasionally; toward the end of the Moustero-Levalloisan stage, it became more common; and after the invention of the chipping of flint into blades, its use flourished. The workman fashioned it by striking once or twice against the end of a blade in such a way as to produce a small transversal cutting edge quite similar to that of a modern plane. It was the main tool for carving bone; its popularity during the age of the reindeer is matched by the development of the art of bone-carving, in which the antlers of the reindeer played an important part.

The scraper also existed long before the age of the reindeer, but on a smaller scale. Its exact use is not known;

hunters probably used it to scrape pelts in much the same way as did the Eskimos and the Fuegians of the last century.

In fact flint-working, which had been continuously perfected since the days of the first Clactonian sliver, reached its apogee during the age of the reindeer. No other important innovation occurred until the beginning of the age of bronze; then came the long blades with their matchless finish, the supreme marvel of the last flint-workers who were competing against the first smelters with their metal daggers.

OTHER RAW MATERIALS: SOFT STONE

Flint and its substitutes were not the only rocks used during the age of the reindeer. Flint gravers were used to work soft stone in much the same way as bone or wood. There are few movable objects of soft stone, but there are numerous engravings and sculptures on the walls of caves. Magnificent horses in bas-relief were discovered at Cap-Blanc and a frieze depicting various animals was found at Roc (France). Recently there was discovered at Angles-sur-l'Anglin a monumental frieze of bisons, horses and wild goats; here the Magdalenian sculptor appears as the equal of the best artists of any age.

WOOD

No wooden object dating from the age of the reindeer has been preserved until the present, but there is indirect evidence that wood-carving was practiced. Slivers of flint from the end of the Mousterian period have all the earmarks of carving tools. Notches and scratches indicate that they were used to rasp wood or bone. Since almost no bone objects from this period have been found, it is logical to conclude that these tools were used to smooth the shafts of assagais, boar-spears, and stakes for digging up edible roots.

Rasping and carving implements dating from the age of

Three Magdalenian objects carved from reindeer antlers: an assagai with a split base, a beveled assagai, and a thick sewing needle. (Plate by G. Tendron.)

the reindeer must have been used on wood as well as on bone. The existence of wooden objects is proved by the thousands of beveled assagais that have been found. Moreover, a score of paintings and engravings show bisons or horses that have been wounded by weapons fashioned from wood. One point is still not clear: we do not know what the men of the age of the reindeer used to cut down trees or saw off thick limbs. All their flint implements are too light for such tasks; they include neither wedges nor anything resembling an axe. If they worked big pieces of wood, the manner in which they approached the task remains to be explained.

BONE, REINDEER ANTLERS, IVORY

Until the age of the reindeer, bone was apparently little used. Occasionally portions of reindeer antlers and bone slivers suitable for use as punches are discovered, but there is nothing comparable to the admirable flint-work of the same period. The poverty of the art of bone-carving is astounding when we consider the skill of the Mousterian artisans and the abundance of bone at their disposal. The end of the Mousterian period offers a few bone implements of better quality, especially punches, but not until the beginning of the age of the reindeer did a flood of new objects suddenly appear: assagais fashioned from reindeer antlers or ivory (from the mammoth), bone punches, pierced teeth to be strung and used as pendants, and ribs trimmed to serve as spatulas or polishers.

SKINS AND TEXTILES

Signs left on the joints of the reindeer by flint knives indicate that the Paleanthropes skinned their game. Just how they used these skins is not known. From the age of the reindeer on, the same markings appear on bones; other finds include many ivory sewing needles, very fine punches made from bone or flint, and big mammoth bones that must have been used as work tables for cutting skin garments, for they bear multiple scratches left by flint cutters.

The needles and punches prove that skins were sewn with threads or thongs. The men of the age of the reindeer may have used plant fibers or strips of bark. That they used the tendons of reindeer or wild goats is certain; the bones of the feet of these animals are often found side by side among sets of implements (and not among garbage heaps); these bones stayed together because they were stacked there with their tendons intact, much like bobbins.

The skins of bears and hyenas were probably used as rugs or coverings, too. On the floors used by the men of the age of the reindeer are found the phalanges and claws of these animals, crushed on the ends and bearing flint marks; these remnants were probably left attached to the skins just as they are in modern bedside rugs.

91

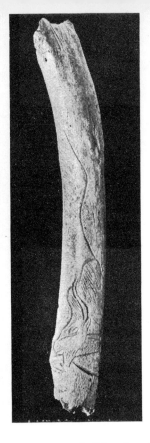

A bison's head engraved on a rib. Magdalenian (from Laugerie, Les Eyzies).
(Plate by Musée de l'Homme.)

METALS, POTTERY

Metal was not used as such during the age of the reindeer. But tons of red ocher (an impure ore of iron) were used to adorn dwelling-places and sepulchers, and occasional lumps of iron ore were collected, probably as curiosities because of their density. In the old Perigordian stage we found, on two different occasions, chunks of galena the size of walnuts; they had probably been collected because of their sparkling crystals.

Not one piece of pottery has been definitely identified among the thousands of stations that have been excavated. The few bits of cooked earth discovered so far were from hearths, which baked the soil around them. The men who lived on the clay floors of caves were apparently unable to use the clay to fashion containers. This is not surprising, for several recent tribes did not use pottery (the nomads of Asia, the American Indians, the Oceanians), and others discarded its use for different reasons (the Ainus and the Eskimos of the northern Pacific).

CULTURAL CURRENTS: PERIGORDIAN

The men of the age of the reindeer belonged to diverse human types. Nor was their civilization uniform. Against a common background, diverse cultural currents developed according to periods and regions.

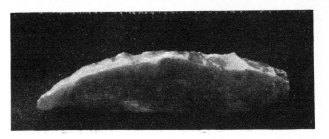

This "jagged-edged blade" or Chatelperron point is characteristic of old Perigordian. The rugged finish of the curved top makes it a knife-blade with a straight cutting edge and a blunt back. (Plate by G. Tendron.)

The *Perigordian* current (so named because of findings in the caves of Perigord) appeared soon after the intermediary period that had followed the Mousterian civilization. During the intermediary period, men had not yet substituted blades for flint slivers but were already making gravers, scrapers and knives. The knives were made from triangular slivers. These slivers were flattened on one side to provide a rough back, like that of the blade of a pocketknife. At the very beginning of the Perigordian stage appeared knives fashioned, no longer from slivers, but from blades. They are called "Chatelperron points." They kept the curved back of the older knives made from slivers. The same tradition lasted throughout the age of the reindeer but with progressive refinements; the back was smoothed down until it became straight, and the knives themselves became smaller.

At the beginning of the Perigordian stage, the Chatelperron point and the gravers were almost the only signs of the appearance of a new cultural stream; then new implements with a rugged finish on one side appeared. At the same time the last traces of the Mousterian stream disappeared, and the Aurignacian stream (see below) brought in new implements, such as the keel-shaped scraper.

Bone objects are relatively few in old Perigordian but include punches and short, flat or cylindrical assagais. The latter were progressively elongated; by the Magdalenian stage, they had become ornate devices a foot long.

93

AURIGNACIAN

The Aurignacian stage is marked by a distinct style of flint-chipping. Heavy implements (the keel-shaped scraper and curved gravers) were finished with fine, light rows of grooves, as were the long, two-edged blades. Both types of objects again appeared in some regions during the Magdalenian stage.

Assagais, especially, were carved from bone. They were short, flat and diamond-shaped, with split bases.

The Perigordian and Aurignacian streams were contemporaneous for a long time, with the result that in different regions all possible combinations of styles are possible: Chatelperron points and keel-shaped scrapers, for instance. This proves clearly that classifications such as Perigordian and Aurignacian stand for technical currents rather than for groups of people with different traditions.

SOLUTREAN

The Solutrean current is found in the southern part of France. The name derives from Solutre (Saône-et-Loire). It separates the Aurignacian and Magdalenian stages. It is characterized by the "point in the shape of a laurel-leaf," the most beautiful flint object of the age of the reindeer.

Keel-shaped scraper. This is a heavy scraper found in the Aurignacian strata. (Plate by G. Tendron.)

The point is finished with flat grooves on both sides, like the small bifaces of the end of the Mousterian stage and some of the early Perigordian points; doubtless they represent the continuation of an old tradition that the Solutrean artisans imported from some region where the thread was unbroken.

Leaf-shaped points were too thin for hand-pikes; they would not have held up under the strain required of such implements. They could have been used effectively only if launched with the great speed of an arrow. There is no proof that the bow was used at that time; wooden objects were not preserved, and no engraving or painting shows a bow. But such a weapon may well have already been in existence.

Against this, we are sure that there was another projectile weapon during the age of the reindeer. It may have been used by Solutrean hunters, and was certainly used by their Magdalenian successors. This weapon was the *propeller,* a board or stick with a loop at the end where the heel of the assagai was placed. A rapid arm and wrist movement launched the assagai with a speed comparable to that of an arrow launched from a bow. This weapon is used by people in different parts of the world today—the Eskimoes, the Australians, the New Guineans, the Indians of Peru, Mexico and California. It is shown in paintings of the age of the reindeer (like those of the Lascaux cave); besides, finds include several samples, carved from reindeer antlers, from the Magdalenian stage. The other objects of the Solutrean current are not always easily distinguished from the recent Aurignacian or middle Magdalenian current except for the fact that the shape of some implements ordinarily show the flat finish characteristic of the laurel-leaf.

Were the Solutreans really a tribe or race? Did they come from the south or the east? Did they infiltrate Aurignacian groups? Or do the laurel-leaf assagais simply represent a technical current which spread with inter-tribal contact? The two hypotheses are not mutually exclusive. It is possible

Solutrean "laurel leaves." These points, long and flat, were attached to the shafts of assagais.

that a tribe that practiced the Solutrean craft came from the outside and settled for several centuries at points in south-western France and along the Saone; some members of established tribes might well have adopted their marvelous and delicate assagais.

MAGDALENIAN

At first the flint-work of the Magdalenian stage differed little from Aurignacian and Perigordian flint-work, follow-ing these styles directly in the regions where there was no Solutrean current. Then it evolved in the direction of tiny pieces and culminated in the style characteristic of the period that followed the age of the reindeer.

The carving of bone and antlers was also a continuation of an older tradition, but here it developed with marked

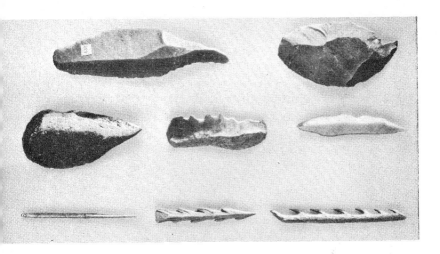

Magdalenian set of implements. Flint implements had become smaller and were designed chiefly for fine carving—ivory, bone, and probably also wood, bark and leather. From left to right, top to bottom, are shown: a "parrot-billed" graver, a hollowed-out blade, a small Gravette point, a saw-toothed blade, a "fluted" graver, an ivory needle and two pieces of harpoons made of reindeer antlers.   (Plate by G. Tendron.)

originality and resulted in the production of propellers and cudgels. The latter were reindeer antlers through which thumb-sized holes had been punched near the ends. These objects, also labeled "commander's cudgels," in all probability were actually used for straightening the points of assagais. For assagais made from the lamellae of reindeer antlers were naturally curved; craftsmen could straighten them by warming them and using the cudgels as levers. Assagais, when found in the course of excavations, have usually reacquired their natural curvature and would accordingly be useless to the hunter. Along with countless Magdalenian assagais are also found, in some regions, harpoons with one or two rows of barbs; they were probably used to catch large fish.

As the carving of bone and reindeer antlers progressed, so did art. From the outset, art characterized the Magdalenian stage. Moreover, the most striking trait of the age of the reindeer as a whole was the appearance of art and religion.

The presence of curiosities and some ocher indicated a rudimentary artistic or religious sense among the last Neanderthalians. But the evidence left by *Homo sapiens* during the age of the reindeer is infinitely greater. Artistic activity began to develop during the middle Aurignacian stage; some beautiful works also survive from the Solutrean stage; and prehistoric art reached its apogee during the period extending from the end .of the Aurignacian to the middle of the Magdalenian stage. This is the great period of plaques engraved with human and animal figures, of thousands of ornate bone carvings, of hundreds of caves containing walls covered with drawings of animals, and of tombs filled with funeral decorations and ocher.

Toward the end of the Magdalenian stage, art changed rapidly. No longer did the walls of caves bear new painted or engraved figures; the design of objects evolved toward progressively more simple forms. The artistic flowering had died out completely by the end of the Würm glaciation.

In sum, the coming of modern man to various regions of France matched the development of a civilization with roots in the Mousterian past but with an intellect much more like our own. When we carefully uncover the floor of

Magdalenian cudgel, also called "commander's cudgel." The name is suggestive but probably signifies nothing. These "cudgels" made of reindeer antlers were probably levers used in straightening heated assagais. Bone arrowheads tended progressively to resume the natural curvature of the antlers from which they were shaped. (Plate by G. Tendron.)

their caves and reconstruct the activities of the hunters of the age of the reindeer—here we see the flat stones used to level holes, here a needle lost between two stones, here an assagai which still bears the marks of the graver used in fashioning it, here a stone lamp with the outline of its wick on its calcined edged—then these men, lost for fifteen or twenty thousand years, seem very near to us. But exactly **what was their daily life like?**

9. HOW PEOPLE LIVED DURING THE AGE OF THE REINDEER

Much more is known about the life and customs of the men of the age of the reindeer than about their Paleanthrope predecessors. The daily life of Augustine had to be reconstructed from scattered snapshots. Against this, it is possible to draw up a coherent account of the life of *Homo sapiens* during the age of the reindeer.

HUNTING AND FISHING

The most commonly used weapons were apparently pikes, assagais and harpoons. We are certain of their existence, at any rate, for flint and bone endured. Weapons made entirely of wood probably existed also—clubs and missiles like the boomerang; but wooden objects disappeared. Moreover, they were of little use against big game. Here as among all big-game hunters before the invention of the rifle, the main weapon was the assagai. The situation in medieval France was no different.

Assagais were probably launched from propellers; except among the Solutreans, they were made not of flint but of ivory or reindeer antlers. Harpoons appeared rather late in the Magdalenian stage; they had detachable points and were tied to thongs which could be played out in much the same way as a fishing line to avoid breakage and to bring in the catch. The harpoon could be used only in the water against big fish or aquatic mammals; on land, the thong would inevitably break when pulled by a strong animal. The Solutreans may also have attached several points to one shaft in such a way as to make a grabber or trident for fishing.

The men of the age of the reindeer probably knew how to trap animals. Like some Indians or the Lapps, they must have surrounded herds of reindeer or horses and stampeded them over cliffs. Or perhaps they simply forced them into long, narrow passes and slaughtered them there. They must have used collars and leashes, but there is no proof of this. A few cave drawings point to the use of ditches or wooden traps designed to capture mammoths or bisons. But the use of tree trunks requires a heavy wood-cutting tool and, as indicated in the last chapter, excavations have revealed no trace of such a tool during the age of the reindeer.

In short, but one fact is certain: the men of this period hunted with the assagai. This implement was, moreover, enough to assure them of a great variety of game. But it leaves unanswered the question of how they managed to dominate mammoths and rhinoceros; the assagai (even when poisoned) was too light to be used as a weapon against these giants with their thick skins. Here, as in the case of the cutting of timber, is an unsolved problem of prehistoric anthropology.

The men of the age of the reindeer also captured many birds. The means used, though not known, were probably varied and similar to those of the Eskimoes: with their hands, with assagais, with stones, and perhaps even with thongs.

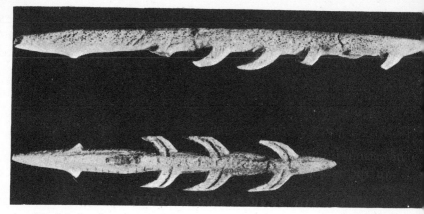

Magdalenian harpoons had detachable heads which were tied to the staffs. They were used for fishing. Presumably, the Magdalenians fished for trout and salmon at stations wherever these harpoons are found. (Plate by G. Tendron.)

PLANT FOODS

The gathering of fruits, grains, sprouts, and roots must have played an important role in the lives of the men of the age of the reindeer. Even among the Eskimoes, who live under much less favorable conditions, plant foods are of some importance.

There is no evidence, even indirect, concerning the plant foods of the men of the age of the reindeer. But the plants at his disposal are known, thanks to the fossil pollens of the period. They were the flora of the northern tundra and marshlands; from them he could take: many berries (like the bilberry), mushrooms, the inner bark of pines and willows from forested areas, tubers and bulbs from plants like the wild lily, green shoots from herbaceous plants, and tender leaves from the willow. No plant could furnish ample supplies for the winter; each served only as a seasonal treat. Before the appearance of agriculture, the regions of France which these men inhabited had only a few of the plant foods grown there today. Not until long after the age of the reindeer had ended were cereals introduced from the southeast and east; and many centuries were to elapse before the adoption of such edible roots as carrots and turnips, and still more before beans and potatoes were introduced.

Thus men of the age of the reindeer did not harvest crops; they gleaned what they could from plants in season. Without game and fish, they could not subsist; fortunately for them, both were plentiful.

THE BEGINNINGS OF ANIMAL HUSBANDRY AND AGRICULTURE

Did the men of the age of the reindeer raise horses? Some scholars think that the horse was already domesticated, but there is no proof of this. More recent tribes with similar economic systems practice neither breeding nor agriculture.

At most it can be assumed that a few bands of men were linked at certain times of the year to herds of wild reindeer in the sense that they moved with them and fed on them. This unilateral association may have constituted an intermediate step between hunting and animal husbandry proper; knowing the successive feeding grounds of a herd and being able to go there in search of provisions is a step toward domestication.

The issue of agriculture is not so doubtful. Not only does the organization of an agrarian society call for economic arrangements which would have been impossible during the age of the reindeer, but also there was no plant in France to serve as a basis for agriculture. At most, men might have removed parasitical plants from spots where edible plants grew wild. Agriculture may have started in some regions as a result of the weeding of wild vegetation.

THE SEARCH FOR MINERALS

In the regions where flint was plentiful, supplies posed no serious problems. Still it was necessary to reach the right layer of the earth and select the chunks that had not been frozen. One need only look for workable flint in order to appreciate the difficulty of this type of prospecting. Even where layers of flint are laid bare in quarries and brick-fields, the task is not easy; it must have been all the more difficult to discover the spots where digging would uncover flint beneath the mantel of grass on the steppe or in the forest. The good sites were doubtless known by tradition; the stone-yards were kept in repair from one generation to the next. In some regions flint deposits at ground level are literally covered with slivers and implements from all periods, from the Acheulean to the bronze age.

During the age of the reindeer, the increased yield of cutting surface per pound of raw material allowed men to live far from their source of flint (see page 86). This suggests that they carried out extensive raids in search of the raw materials which were essential to the life of the group; doubtless they also carried on trade. Scientists have studied the microscopic structure of the flints of a few stations with a view to determining their geographical origin, but their studies have not yet yielded decisive results.

Other studies have furnished information about the transporting of objects over great distances. Men of the age of the reindeer collected shells and punched holes through them in order to make head-dresses or necklaces. Some shells from the seashore have been found many miles away from the sea; other fossil shells from the sands near Paris were found at Arcy-sur-Cure, more than sixty miles away. These include serpent-stones and trilobites like the pierced pendant for which one of the Arcy caves was named. At Arcy we also found pebbles brought from afar because of their crystal sheen. Their presence shows that men of the age of the reindeer sometimes transported objects over great distances.

COOKERY

All that is known about culinary practices is that there were numerous hearths. But no one has yet found a receptacle, a ladle or a spoon. Perhaps there were bark or skin receptacles, horn or wooden spoons, but no trace of them has been found.

Perhaps men of the age of the reindeer ate their food raw, like some Eskimoes who, having no combustibles, consume meat and fish raw, sometimes with salt. Perhaps they were like some Indians who, knowing nothing of pottery, put hot stones into their bark pots and thus produce excellent broth; or perhaps they were like the Australians who grill and roast with live coals. Finally, there is no reason why they might not have combined the three systems.

CLOTHING

The cutting implements that have been discovered indicate that men of the age of the reindeer made their clothing from animal skins. As for the nature and shape of these garments, the artistic productions of the period are somewhat disconcerting.

These works of art include a large number of statues, bas-reliefs, and engravings of both men and women. The women wear no clothing. But this does not necessarily mean that they strolled around in this fashion. Otherwise some ten thousand years hence future scholars might discover one of our contemporary art galleries and draw erroneous conclusions about feminine attire of the twentieth century. As for the men represented by the artists of the age of the reindeer, they are sometimes dressed, but in a rather curious fashion: they are disguised as reindeer or as horses. They are probably sorcerers or dancers, or hunters camouflaged to deceive their game. Prehistoric art doubtless aimed only at conventional representations, corresponding sometimes to magi-

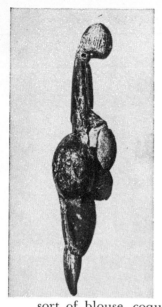

This ivory statuette is the most beautiful of the Paleolithic statuettes. It comes from the Lespugne cave (Haute-Garonne). It is extremely stylized and is probably no more representative of paleolithic women than are some modern sculptures representative of the average contemporary French woman.
(Plate by Musée de l'Homme.)

cal rites; it was not concerned with the realistic representation of domestic life.

Fortunately there is one exception. A Magdalenian bas-relief showing the bust of a man was recently discovered at Angles-sur-l'Anglin. He has a snub nose and bare head and wears a rather commonplace sort of blouse, coquettishly set off by a necklace and some decorative details. Thanks to this bust, our ivory needles and bobbins made of tendons finally find their place.

HOME

Because the best sites were discovered in caves, it has sometimes been wrongly supposed that prehistoric men systematically chose this type of domicile. They did so only where there were caves and perhaps for want of anything better, with the exception of caves which were especially well located and sufficiently large and dry.

But all other habitations have disappeared while caves have been preserved. That is why they are the focal point of studies in prehistory, though numerous heaps of worked flint prove that men also lived out in the open. And though not a single structure dating from the age of the reindeer has been uncovered in France, several have been found in Ukraine.

At Kostienki, near Kiev, a veritable Solutrean village was

discovered. It has a row of open-air hearths surrounding storage-pits and habitations. One hut is fairly well preserved. It consisted of two adjoining oval-shaped rooms dug into the ground to a depth of about a yard and having a diameter of five or six yards. A bench circled the rooms, serving as both a seat and a bed. On the bench was a column of mammoth tusks, set up to support the roof. Sod or turf must have been placed on a layer of big mammoth bones, especially shoulder and pelvic bones, to form the roof. Its occupants contrasted sharply with the wandering hordes who sought the shelter of an overhang.

It is not unusual to find living quarters next to a cliff, or "sheltered nooks" dominated by an overhang. Such spots were well protected and often more comfortable than caves. It was enough to throw windbreakers made of boughs against the wall, or perhaps a tent made of skins or an embankment of sod. Most sheltered nooks, if studied carefully, show that such structures once existed; moreover, many walls have rings carved into them, and these rings were probably used to anchor tents.

Last but not least come the well-kept caves. The floor was generally level; to keep the cave dry, the occupants often spread out layers of stones, sometimes forming a sort of flagstone pavement. Gradually on this surface were heaped broken and worn-out tools, pendants with broken strings, small particles of food passed over in sweeping, and other tiny bits of debris. Dirt brought in by the occupants' feet gradually covered those vestiges, which now form thin strata classified chronologically.

Living centered around the entrance of the cave; the living quarters rarely extended farther than thirty yards within the cave. Near the entrance was the hearth. Combustibles must have been scarce, for there are few ashes other than those of calcined reindeer bones. With meat and marrow removed, the broken bones fed the flame. Combustibles were

used sparingly; ashes are sometimes scattered over several square yards, but the hearth itself generally is no larger than a table napkin. It is sometimes slightly below ground level, rarely lined with stones. Like every open hearth, it provided both heat and light. In several places traces of strange heating devices have been found: a pile of pebbles or gravels was heaped on live coals; the pebbles stored the heat, serving as a veritable hot-air stove. This system was similar to the stoves used in the cold parts of Europe and the Finnish *sauna,* or steam bath, prepared by pouring water over hot stones.

The hearth was not the only source of light. Several Magdalenian lamps have been found. They were very similar to lamps used by some Eskimoes. They were fashioned by filling hollow stones with lard and inserting wicks. The cave dwellers also used torches, especially juniper torches, which left traces on the spots where they were snuffed against the walls. Torches were used by those who wandered deep inside the caves, to the far recesses where artists executed their frescoes.

ART AND RELIGION

The most fascinating aspect of the civilization of the age of the reindeer is the development of religion and art. The famous paintings of the Lascaux cave are often compared to the great frescoes of classic art, the horses of the bas-reliefs of Angles-sur-l'Anglin to those of the Parthenon, the painted caves to temples. The most recent of these works was created at least ten thousand years ago—four times the span that separates the present from early Greek art. Even at that remote time there were men who painted mammoths realistically.

The men of the age of the reindeer must have had a system of religious beliefs, but there is little to give a clue to its essentials. Imagine trying to deduce the system of Christianity from nothing more than crucifixes and church statues!

Here the chief witnesses are all the objects which go be-

The floor of a Magdalenian habitation in the Saint-Marcel cave (Indre.) The white arrows point to assagais made from reindeer antlers and to several flint implements left lying on the floor. (Plate by A. Leroi-Gourhan.)

The biggest Magdalenian lamp yet uncovered came from the Saint-Marcel cave (Indre). The natural hollow in the stone block was deepened and enlarged. Through the depressions along the sides were passed wicks which left clearly defined traces of burns on the stone. The fuel was probably fat from the reindeer or horse or tallow from the aurochs. (Plate by Dr. Allain.)

yond practical utility. It is not always possible to untangle the religious and the artistic:

(1) Red ocher. It is found in almost all sepulchers but was in no way necessary for burying a corpse.

(2) Engravings on harpoons. A plain harpoon would have killed salmon just as effectively.

(3) Pierced shells. Shell necklaces were not necessary for comfortable living.

(4) Statuettes of women, paintings and engravings in the depths of caves. They did nothing to improve living conditions.

The catalogue of the museum of prehistory suggests that the preoccupations of the men of the age of the reindeer clearly went beyond the strict material requirements. To distinguish next between what belongs to art, to religion or to magic would pose difficult philosophical problems. A simple description of these objects is more practical

OCHER

Ferruginous ocher is rather common, especially in regions with calcareous soil, where caves are generally located. The last Mousterians were beginning to use it; from the outset of the Perigordian or Aurignacian stage, its use was common. Its color varies from yellow to red and brown, depending on its ore content and state (raw or calcined). It was a

Solutrean horses in bas-relief found in a sheltered nook at Mouthiers (Charente).
(Plate by A. Leroi-Gourhan.)

basic pigment for the cave painters. It probably had other uses, too, but little is known about them.

Finds frequently include bits of ocher shaped like pencils, or pieces with smooth facets, or flat stones on which the coloring was ground. All this suggests that many things besides designs in the depths of caves were painted red. Perhaps the men painted their faces in the same way as the Australians or the Indians; perhaps they tinted their weapons in the same way as the Eskimoes of Alaska; or perhaps they decorated animal skins and barks in the same way as many recent tribes.

In almost every grave dating from the age of the reindeer, the skeletal remains were found lying in a layer of ocher. Was ocher the symbol of blood and life? Was it a luxury as well as a defense against the dead? Was it a palliative offered the dead to protect the living from revenge? In any event, ocher was connected in some way with a rite of religious significance.

Finally, ocher was scattered on the floors of caves. At some stations the intensity of the red coloring is striking. Several strata of the Arcy cave are good examples. The middle Aurignacian stratum is extraordinary: on the clearly-defined pavement marking the living quarters lies a covering of violet-red ocher, almost pure except for the minute debris left by daily living. The layer varies in thickness from four to eight inches. The hundreds of pounds of ocher found in the cave were carried from the opposite bank of a stream, a distance of about half a mile. Was all the ocher spread on the pavement at one time to make a rug-like covering? Or was the beautiful carpet refurbished from time to time by the addition of a few pounds of new ocher? What is the significance of the excessive indulgence in the use of the colorful material? It is possible that red, the color of blood, was to the hunters both a magical symbol and a sign of wealth?

THE DEAD

Scores of sepulchers dating from the age of the reindeer have been found in Europe. The deceased is sometimes stretched full length, sometimes not. Sometimes a few stones protect his head, and always there is a pit. Generally the body was interred with ornaments: a shell hairnet on the head, necklaces, and a few bone or flint objects.

Leaving the personal objects of the living on the corpse of the dead suggests fear of contamination by death or of revenge on the part of the dead; it also suggests that the living prepared the dead for life in another world. Magical contamination by objects of the dead, though not necessarily presuming an afterlife, takes on a religious character. The other two hypotheses imply a belief in another life. The protection given the head seems clearly to show also that the corpse was not thought of as being wholly deprived of the faculties of the living.

In all these acts, the men of the age of the reindeer resemble modern man closely. Though we do not know their religious beliefs in detail, we are sure of their existence.

DECORATED OBJECTS

Excavations have revealed hundreds of assagais, harpoons, propellers, eyed cudgels and punches, all bearing engraved or sculptured figures, generally representing animals. Magic

A grave in a Grimaldi cave (Menton). The skeleton was moved in the form shown to the Musée de l'Homme. This photograph was taken in 1872, soon after the grave had been uncovered. The skeleton, slightly curved, was surrounded by funeral furnishings consisting of bone and flint objects. The cranium still bore a hairnet made of small pierced shells.
(Plate by Emile Rivière.)

may have motivated these works: an assagai depicting a reindeer might reach its mark more surely than another. But quite probably also, the artist worked for pleasure, and religious art overlapped daily living, with no clear-cut line of demarcation between the two.

Some plaques of soft stone, some bones that served no known purpose were covered with engravings of animals or of diverse scenes. These works were doubtless of the same general significance as those that adorn the walls of caves (see below). There are also some statuettes and engravings depicting women. Is such a work the portrait of the beloved mate of a hunter? Is it the goddess of the harvest?

CAVE SANCTUARIES

Some murals have been found at the entrances of caves or under overhangs, but most are hidden in the depths of caves. Some works were executed in spacious corridors or easily accessible rooms, near or far from daylight. Others— the majority—were produced under extraordinary condi-

113

tions, hundreds of yards from the entrance, beyond whirl-pools or difficult passageways, in recesses where the artist had to work from a prone position, in spiraling tunnels where he had to crawl like a cat and inch his way upward like a chimney-sweep. Obviously, the artist did not make his way into such places and paint the walls just for pastime: simply by their location, these works suggest the existence of sanctuaries.

The walls of caves bear representations of many animals, apparently arranged in no definite pattern. Often the shape of the surface was used to bring out contours. The bison's head was placed beside a ridge to suggest the animal's profile; a horse was placed in such a way as to have a natural depression emphasize his chubby flank; a fault in the rock suggested the spine; or a stalactite resembling a trunk served as a starting point for a picture of a mammoth. The species most often pictured are those commonly used for food: horses, reindeer, wild goats, bison and wild cattle. Less frequently, the artists depicted the giant animals, mammoths and rhinoceros; less frequently still, such predatory animals as the lion, bear and wolf. Sometimes representations of other animals are found: the musk ox, hyena, deer, hare, owl.

Most of these animals, surprisingly well executed, are depicted without commentary—walking, browsing, or motionless as if suspended. Only their strange location deep within a cave suggests that they were placed there for some religious purpose.

But from time to time more revealing figures are found. They show animals wounded by the hunter. At Lascaux, a complete scene is enacted: a bison is disemboweled by a long spear and his entrails are spilling out, but he is still able to knock down a hunter. At Montespan in the Pyrenees, a horse is engraved on the clay next to a wall; it served as a target, for the holes made by assagais are still visible. A little beyond, two clay bears were found; they, too, had been riddled

The "mammoth with the out-stretched trunk" is one of eighteen engravings found in the Horse's cave at Arcy. The engravings were executed as a group. They cover the walls of two rooms located about a hundred yards from the entrance and at the end of an almost inaccessible corridor. Most of them owe their relief to irregularities in the wall. Here the mammoth's eye and hair are made more vivid by a natural depression which accents the work of the graver. (Plate by Emperaire.)

by assagais. Doubtless the hunters used magical charms; they used magic to "kill" their game in the caves in the hope that they might achieve their aim more effectively on the outside. The cave sanctuaries may also have been used as places to initiate future hunters. There, in those mysterious surroundings, they may have been taught the secrets of grown men, especially the rites to be observed in hunting. In the Ariège cave, near two modeled bisons, adolescent footprints were found.

Careful study of cave drawings reveals that two or three periods are intermixed and superimposed almost everywhere.

The faded sanctuaries were apparently restored from time to time, as in the case of our churches. This observation fits in with the notion of a prearranged setting designed to terrorize novices and fill them with awe.

Other representations are enigmatic. Some show masked men dressed as fantastic animals. In some caves hands coated with ocher left their imprints on the wall; elsewhere, the outlines of hands were traced. In still other caves are found inexplicable signs suggesting huts, stiles, perhaps even traps.

Such is the overall picture of the age of the reindeer. Thanks to the patience of men engaged in research during the last three quarters of a century, we now know more about the lives of the men of the distant past than about the lives of some modern tribes.

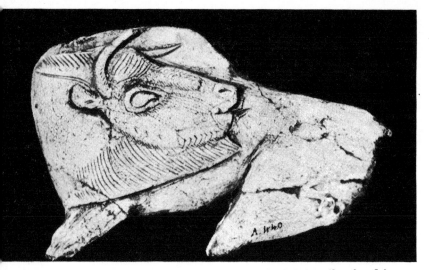

A Magdalenian engraving of a bison on a piece of reindeer antler, found in La Madeleine cave. This is a beautiful example of the embellishing of commonplace objects used by men of the age of the reindeer. The artist utilized both the shape and function of the object (probably the crook of an arrow propeller) to best advantage in showing a bison turning around to lick its flank. (Plate by Monuments historiques.)

10. THE END OF PREHISTORIC TIMES

The last glaciation ran its course. About eight thousand years before our era, the last reindeer started northward for the last time. The cold continental climate gave way to the temperate Atlantic climate familiar to the French today. The steppe and tundra dotted thickly with horses and reindeer were replaced by groves of walnut and the beautiful oak and beech forest traversed only by small bands of squirrels and wild boars. From that time onward, game was scarce and played only a secondary role in alimentation, for men could no longer depend on it for food during the whole year. Contrary to what one might have supposed, the return to a mild climate marked, along with the end of the civilization of the age of the reindeer, the beginning of difficult times.

The long period of time studied in this book—from the

dark beginnings of humanity until the end of the age of the reindeer—is usually lumped together and classed by students of prehistory as *paleolithic* ("old stone age"). Then came the *neolithic* ("new stone age"), which was also the age of the first metals. Between the two was a "middle age," the *mesolithic*.

The mesolithic period left fewer traces in France than the Mousterian or the age of the reindeer. Humanity had fallen back to an inferior economic and cultural level in France. During the age of the reindeer, western Europe had been one of the great zones of civilization, as is evidenced by the cave sanctuaries of France and Spain. During the mesolithic period, great events were unfolded elsewhere: to the north, toward the Baltic, where climatic conditions were the same as those of France during the preceding period, and especially to the south, in the eastern Mediterranean, where the civilization of historical times was already developing. The moment when agriculture and animal husbandry, metallurgy and writing were to appear in succession in these regions—that moment was at hand. In France during the same period, small groups of men settled along the banks of streams or along the coasts, living still by fishing and gathering plant foods. Some, in the Pyrenees and in Provence, fed mainly on snails.

About three thousand years before our era the neolithic civilization, based on agriculture and animal husbandry, reached western Europe. Between twenty-five hundred and three thousand years before our era, copper objects were introduced to France. Shortly thereafter came bronze. But here the student of prehistory must make way for the historian, and this book was intended to outline only paleolithic developments.

The paleolithic period covered one age in the evolution of humanity. From the Archanthropes with their choppers to *Homo sapiens* and the frescoes on the walls of the Lascaux cave, we follow the same current across changes of

118

climate and men. That world lasted at least a hundred times longer than ours, and now it seems to us as if it existed on another planet. It died at the same time as its monsters, the mammoths and wooly rhinoceros. After it, civilization was to be completely rebuilt on different bases: grain would require a granary, which would in turn call for a rampart for its defense, troops to man the rampart, and a scribe to count the sacks of wheat, impose duties and chronicle events. If *Homo sapiens* and grain had made their appearance at the same time, we might assume that the paleolithic and neolithic worlds belonged to different branches of mankind, that they were distinct. But now we know that our peer, *Homo sapiens,* played the last act of the paleolithic drama before he made his entrance on the modern stage.

Without the science of prehistory, the most marvelous and mysterious side of our destiny would be beyond our reach. Historical times represent but a few minutes in the long day of mankind. If we knew only what recorded history reveals, we would know nothing of the obstinate struggle waged by man in his effort to attain his goal.

If cave-diggers had not listened to Augustine, we would have mistaken notions about the infancy of humanity. Augustine probably did not understand much about philosophy or modern commerce, but she was well acquainted with the works of her time. This large, ungainly creature probably had the brain of a three-year-old child, but such a child possesses in a rudimentary fashion the qualities of the adult.

To study prehistory by satisfying one's curiosity about odd knickknacks—pebbles and broken bones—would be pointless: singing birds and babbling brooks are of greater interest. But to use what is known of the past in order better to understand man, is to pay tribute to the thousands of beings who died in transmitting to their successors the secret of the fabrication of the biface, until the day when their successors decided that they had become "wise men."

119

INDEX

The numbers in dark type refer to illustrations.